BOOKS BY KURT W. MAREK (*C. W. CERAM*)

YESTERMORROW   (1961)

BOOKS BY C. W. CERAM (*KURT W. MAREK*)

THE MARCH OF ARCHAEOLOGY   (1958)

THE SECRET OF THE HITTITES   (1956)

GODS, GRAVES, AND SCHOLARS   (1951)

THESE ARE BORZOI BOOKS
PUBLISHED IN NEW YORK BY
ALFRED A. KNOPF, INC.

YESTERMORROW

NOTES
ON
MAN'S
PROGRESS

YESTERMORROW

NEW YORK   ALFRED A. KNOPF 1961

NOTES
ON
MAN'S
PROGRESS

WITH A GLOSSARY-INDEX

by
Kurt W. Marek
(C. W. Ceram)

TRANSLATED FROM
THE GERMAN BY
Ralph
Manheim

L. C. catalog card number: 61–13218

THIS IS A BORZOI BOOK,

PUBLISHED BY ALFRED A. KNOPF, INC.

Manufactured in the United States of America.
Published simultaneously in Canada
by McClelland & Stewart, Ltd.

FIRST AMERICAN EDITION

Originally published in German
as *Provokatorische Notizen,*
© 1960 by Kurt W. Marek.

Publisher's Note

The expressions "high cultures" and "civilization"
occurring in the text are used throughout by the author
in the sense given to them by the German philosopher
of history Oswald Spengler.

Spengler's "high cultures," such as the Chinese, the
Egyptian, the Greco-Roman, and our Western culture,
each of which lasted about a 1,000 years, were all
"organic" social structures having a biological life
cycle: youth, maturity, old age, and death.

According to this view, the history of mankind for the
last 5,000 years is marked not by simple continuity,
but rather by the appearance, side by side and
successively, of about two dozen analogous "high
cultures" differing in their subjective aspects but
exhibiting a surprisingly similar sequence of the
same characteristics in the course of their historical
development.

One such characteristic is that in *all* the high
cultures the last, declining phase is marked by a
withering of ideal values, a diminution of creative
energies and of the myth-making power, a thorough
"technification" and rationalization of life. It is only
this last phase of the high cultures which
Spengler designates as a "civilization."

Mr. Marek views the "decline" of the last of the
great high cultures without regret. In contrast to
Spengler, he recognizes in the unprecedented *global*
extension of the latest "civilization" many indications—

v

above all, the hitherto unparalleled phenomenon of
technology itself—presaging for the first time in
5,000 years a deep-reaching crisis of accelerated
change in *all* of human life. It is not the rise of a
new "high culture," in the old sense, which is in the
offing, but a new global order that has little use
for nearly all the values of the past high cultures and,
indeed, can do quite well without them. This new
order will be logically, and to an unprecedented
degree, determined by technology. And the author
takes a positive view of it.
The translation of the term "metaphysische
Aufladung," which comes up repeatedly, presented a
problem. Akin to the process of "charging" an
electric battery, "Aufladung" in the original was
intended to suggest the infusion or enrichment of a
historical work of art, for example, with additional
metaphysical meaning. Although "to charge" would be
a precise translation of the term, it is not strong
enough in English. Hence the word used most of the
time at the request of the author has been "infusion."

An unusual feature of this book is that the index
contains a glossary. "Notes," such as those that make
up this text, by their very nature cannot provide a
full exposition of references, and so we hope that
readers will use the glossary-index freely.

What the Notes are About

A few Notes of a General Nature

*Notes
on
Technology*

*Notes on
Religion,
Metaphysics,
and
Causality*

*On Forms,
on "Art"
and on
Metaphysical
Infusion*

*Notes
On
Literature
In the
Most
General
Sense*

YESTERMORROW

NOTES
ON
MAN'S
PROGRESS

About the
Point
of
View

A few of these notes were written between 1945 and 1948; most of them from 1958 to 1960. They are actual notes, though of course some sandpapering was done before they were sent to the printer.

This remark seems necessary because I should not like these "notes" to be taken for aphorisms. You lift an aphorism up and let it sparkle; these "notes" were not made to sparkle, but to be looked through. The thought they express does not emanate *from* a single point, but tends *toward* a single point. As a writer, I try to conduct myself like a Cartesian diver, moving freely up and down through the various strata of culture and opinion, lingering where it seems worthwhile to linger. This function of the writer, which may be described as a constant quest for orientation, was taken for granted in the days of the Encyclopedists, and should be recaptured. It is rounded out by Ortega y Gasset's stern insistence that a writer must "be constantly on guard against his own convictions."

To suspect one's own convictions excludes the possibility of creating a system. My method of approaching problems can perhaps best be described as one of investment or siege. Let us suppose that the approximate position of an enemy fort is known to us, but that we know nothing else about it. We encircle it and start building trenches of varying depth and length toward it from all sides. The ultimate test of our tactics is, of course, whether or not we capture the fort. I cannot pretend to have got that far, nor, it seems to me, has anyone else. But encirclement is the first step in a decisive attack.

Such trenches will, of necessity, vary in length and depth; in digging them one will encounter matter of varying hardness. Consequently, it

5

would be unjust to criticize our tactics before investigating *all* the trenches, the deep ones, the long ones, and even the shallow ones. Accordingly, any criticism based only on the notes on "art," taking no account of the preceding notes on "technology," would be unjustified.

These "notes" take up a position beyond optimism or pessimism. For the sake of clarity, it is necessary to register certain losses, but I refuse to lament over them, for I am interested in the gains.

It is in the nature of such "notes" that there should be a certain amount of apodictic formulation. And also that they should contain contradictions. But freedom from contradiction is a requirement of "systems"—and here I am not making the slightest attempt to set up a system. A writer has no choice; he must first encompass his world in space and time. He must move from yesterday to tomorrow—yestermorrow.

The nature of this book is such that a wise reader will take it only in homeopathic doses. But often it is the homeopathic dose that has the catalytic quality I am concerned with here, a quality that cannot be overestimated.

A Few
Notes
of a
General
Nature

Certain words in the language have lost their warmth. *The loss of*
Town and village used to be *home;* metropolis *warmth in*
and suburb are, at best, a place to live. The home *language*
included the *hearth* which people tended, and
around which they gathered; the modern dwelling
offers steam heat and a gas stove, which people pay
for, and make use of.

⊙

Architecture has been termed *frozen music.* But no
secular edifice since the Rococo period gives us
this feeling. If a Gothic cathedral is a frozen fugue, a
skyscraper is a frozen electric-bell signal; *frozen
music* has given way to *frozen noise.*

⊙

In the cathedral, moreover, bells rang; their sound,
summoning to prayer or giving warning of fire
and war, became a high symbol of European culture.
The modern counterpart of the bell is the siren.

⊙

It is a part of the same change of atmosphere that *Brother*
"brother" has been replaced by "comrade" as a *and*
term of address. The former (until the middle of the *comrade*
nineteenth century) signalized a bond between a man
and his neighbor, who knew themselves to be
united in faith; the latter bespeaks a utilitarian
community (the socialist organizations in Europe
since 1869), *united under a doctrine.*

⊙

To the Gothic arch with its upward-striving tension
(the overcoming of the material) corresponds
the steel bridge span with its disturbing tension

9

(utilization of the material). In the cathedral the laws
of statics are mastered (we no longer feel oppressed
by them); in the case of the cantilevered concrete
slab, they are strained (and with them, our nerves).
We feel *and* know that the cathedral will stand firm; we
know that the cantilevered slab is safe (but is it?).

⊙

A tempting speculation: to what degree are the
natural sounds of culture characterized by rich vowels
and technological sounds of civilization by a
concert of hissing consonants? Here again we
might take the bell and the siren as our starting points.

⊙

*The sig-
nificance
of light*

Too little attention has been paid to the significance
of light. The "dark" Middle Ages *were* dark, only
the sun gave light. Pine knots and torches, candles
and oil lamps served the extreme functions of
satisfying needs (always) and of enhancing festive
joy (infrequent and socially restricted). Light bulbs
and neon tubes no longer "cast light on," they
no longer "pierce the shadows"; they *flood* with
light, robbing every last corner of its private darkness.

⊙

*Posthumous
infusion*

The Russian thinker Berdyayev sets up two opposing
series: SYMBOLIC—HIERARCHIC—ORGANIC and
REALISTIC—DEMOCRATIC—MECHANICAL! Essentially,
this is the Spenglerian distinction between culture and
civilization (in the Spenglerian order). Nowadays we
run into a good many distinctions of this kind.
    Such distinctions, like the observation of a loss
of warmth in language (words such as myth,
destiny, soul, symbol have turned stone cold by now)

10

are useful as long as they do not lead to sentimental
commentaries. It is not true, as has hitherto been
supposed, that culture is intentionally or naturally
prolific of symbols; symbols have been subsequently
read into the cultures by thinkers conditioned by
an era of civilization. There are, indeed, a number of
values that have been deliberately invented. It is a
case of posthumous infusion.

⊙

The philosophy of culture since the turn of the century
has not been sceptical, pessimistic, or nihilistic, but
sentimental. If we consider the attributes that
have been posthumously infused into culture, we find
that there has been no loss, but only a change.
Since we have to live in the midst of, and after, a
change, it is more important to investigate the gains
than to deplore the losses. "Let the dead bury
their dead."

⊙

Modern analyses of culture are balance sheets ending
with a debit; the bookkeepers have not been mistaken
in their calculations, they have merely overlooked
the fact that scrap metal can be valuable when
melted down.

*The worth-
lessness of
unfavorable
cultural bal-
ance sheets*

⊙

In using the words "culture" and "civilization"
respectively, we must remember that, to each, many
meanings have accrued. The expression "to cultivate"
has to do with the tilling of the soil, with "making
fertile"; the value lies in the operation, not in the
object to which it is applied—there are cultures
of mold. "To civilize" is "to bring refined customs";

11

but when we speak of bringing civilization to a
country, we mean that we are introducing technology.

⊙

War, incidentally, is an achievement of the high
cultures of the past. To this day certain primitive
peoples, such as the Eskimos and the Australian
aborigines, have no proper word for it. It seems
certain that the prehistoric peoples, not to mention the
first Hominidae and the animals, fought, but
they did not make war. If "war" not only originated
with the high cultures but seems inseparable from
them, it is probably safe to assume that it will
also end with them.

◎

Three varie-
ties of utopia

Three types of utopia can be distinguished; they are
seldom consciously mixed, but when they are,
as in H. G. Wells, the mixture is worthy of note.

First, the *reformist* utopias. They spring from a
feeling that the existing world is urgently in need of
ethical and social betterment; they are based on faith
in progress and on wishful thinking. (From
Thomas More's *Utopia* to Edward Bellamy's *Looking
Backward.*)

Secondly, the *playful* utopias. These came into
being with the development of machinery, when men
became fascinated with the notion that one need
only press a button to release any desired effect.
(From Jules Verne to the deluge of American science
fiction.)

Thirdly, the *mene-tekel* utopias. These are the

12

most curious of all, for they unfold prospects of
which their authors do not approve. The authors show
to what an extent the wishful thinking of the reformist
utopians has crystallized into realities, but where
their predecessors envisioned these realities with
enthusiasm, they see them with horror. (From
Aldous Huxley through George Orwell down to
Michael Young's "meritocracy," postulated as "I.Q.
plus effort = merit.")

⊙

Whereas the original utopias, the never-never lands of
wishful thought, were always *blueprints* for a *desirable*
state of affairs, the mene-tekel utopias involve
insights into things to come. That the authors
themselves are indissolubly bound to their
traditional ideals is demonstrated by the fact that
they issue senseless *warnings* against the inevitable,
instead of trying to understand it objectively.

⊙

Of course this classification of utopias is meaningful
only in the light of history. The individual
fantasies have a value of their own quite apart from
this conception. Two forgotten books have taken
the most extreme positions: first, the second volume of
Mathematical Magick by Bishop John Wilkins,
published in 1648, in which the possibility of human
colonies beneath the sea is discussed (a project
with which we shall soon no doubt have to familiarize
ourselves); second, *L'Ève future* by Villiers
de l'Isle-Adam, published in 1886, an absurd satire
in which Edison is made to manufacture an artificial
woman and the idea is carried (philosophically)

*Cities
beneath the
sea*

to its most absurd implications (actually, "artificial life" has today become an urgent problem).

The need for new fictions

Human thinking within a cultural community, a cultural epoch, or even a mere group united by social or ideal ties, goes on as though inside a hothouse through whose opaque walls a dim reflection of another world may be discerned; sometimes perhaps even a "new dawn." Within the hothouse the traditional ideals are enclosed, the notions we may still legitimately call "fictions," as defined by Vaihinger. Within the hothouse, these almost innumerable ideas may be varied and combined quite freely. One of the most difficult ventures of the human spirit is to attempt to break out of the hothouse. This is what the modern mene-tekel utopians are trying to do. They have managed to break through one small window pane, profiting by the damage already done to the cultural hothouse by the first steam hammers, the guiding and shattering lightning of electricity, and the liberation, followed by harnessing, of atomic energies. They have gained a glimpse of vast strange landscapes, but they interpret these through their traditional "fictions."

It is interesting to note that in the familiar high cultures of the past, art achieved its most extreme dimensions in the very earliest times. In the ziggurats, the pyramids, and the early colossi, dimensions were established that have never been greatly exceeded. From Babylonian times until quite recently, an

14

occasional surpassing of the limits has been looked
upon and punished as hubris (until recent times—for
the notion of hubris has lost all meaning in the
era of technology). The man of the old high cultures
saw himself as the natural physical measure of all things.

⊙

Even the building of the Eiffel Tower was no longer
looked upon as hubris. Thus far no importance
has been attached to this fact, because the
Eiffel Tower was not regarded as an "expression of
something," but merely as a curiosity, and indeed
(from our twentieth century vantage point) that is
pretty much what it is.

⊙

The man of the traditional high cultures looked upon
extra-human velocities not only as unattainable, but
as *alien*—a clear expression of his attachment to
himself as measure. Even in connection with arrows
or lightning, he spoke of inconceivable speeds. He
was still able to accept the relatively rapid airplane
of the forties as an *intensification* of a conceivable
motion. The bursting of the sound barrier, however,
and still more the velocities attained by satellites and
space ships, have for the first time brought man
into contact with velocities that exceed all human
measure.

*Man is not
the measure
of all things*

⊙

Among attempts of the human imagination to break
away from the human image in art, those of
Hieronymus Bosch and of Pieter Brueghel the Younger
are instructive. None of their creatures actually

15

represent a break with human (or corresponding
animal) forms and proportions; they are mere variants.

⊙

Man's in-
ability to
depart from
the human
measure

Typical of man's inability thus far to escape from
the human dimension are the attempts of "artists"
in this period, when the stars are coming closer
to us, to imagine inhabitants of Mars. What they
portray is still in man's dimensions, though physically
deformed or technically complicated. The same holds
good when they suppose the planet to be inhabited
by animals—usually favoring insects and rightly so.

⊙

In regard to language, which likewise reflects the
measure of man, Rivarol made the astute remark:
"In man as in language everything is measure" (he
forgot to add that language also is the measure of
man). "One cannot say: 'I saw a flea stretched
out lengthwise,' although from a logical point of view
this would be just as true of a flea as of a calf."
Thus we must add that the measure has not only the
upper limit of the pyramids but also a lower limit.

⊙

Actually the first "inconceivable" forms were not
invented; they were *discovered* beyond the threshold of
our unaided senses. These forms, made visible by
the electron microscope for example, are better
called *structures*.

⊙

Technologists also had difficulty, even when they
began to aim at functional forms, in breaking away
from forms for which the human environment had only
too long provided the proportions. The makers of

16

automobiles had the greatest difficulty in casting
off the form of the horse-drawn wagon, and to
this day even the swiftest jets have not completely
broken away from the image of the bird in flight.
Meanwhile, to be sure, the first purely functional forms
of the plane have been developed—several variants
of the so-called "flying saucers"—which are free
from the preconceptions of nineteenth century man.

⊙

For the development of forms is dictated by the
conditions under which these forms must prove
themselves. Although many such conditions have been
recognized by us today, we are not yet able to
accept the forms to which necessity has given rise.
The present plans for space ships do not give us a
direct picture of the exact purpose they are intended
to serve; our traditionally constricted feeling is
repelled by the idea that these rings or bristle-armored
sets of globes should dash through space at barely
conceivable velocities. But the "saucers" of the
United States Navy, which are already operative, give
us an intimation that the aesthetic strictures of the
nineteenth century are no longer the determining factor.

*Discrepancy
between our
feeling and
the new forms*

⊙

In the nineteen-twenties the aesthetic charms of
functionalism were discovered, as, for example, the
beauty of the streamline. *This* aesthetics has been
invalidated by the new forms.

⊙

To say that man limited his works to the measure of
his natural dimensions means that, as long as man was
the measure of all things, he created nothing that he

17

could not directly govern or control by the activity
of his body or his senses. For example, he built
no tower he could not climb and constructed no
weapon whose effect he could not observe with his
own eyes.

New forms in the "arts."   More clearly than in the sciences the abandonment of
man as a measure has been discernible in painting.
But even in sculpture which, from Michelangelo to
Maillol and Lehmbruck, was exclusively governed by
the image of man, the departure from this image,
begun by Archipenko, is evident. This coincided with
the conquest of new materials (metal, glass, enamel,
wire) which deprived sculptures of their corporeity and
brought them closer to artifacts. In constructions
such as Richard Lippold's variations on the sun and
moon, gigantic golden structures of brass wire,
chrome nickel and stainless steel, the discussion of a
possible "artistic value," such as was sought in the
nineteenth century, becomes meaningless. These
patterns of metal whose charm cannot be defined
by a classical aesthetician, have their counterpart in
the lacework of color with which the American painter
Jackson Pollock, in the last years of his life,
covered canvases sixteen feet long.

The new forms can be understood only with the
help of a new aesthetics that must be kept free of the
metaphysical admixtures of the nineteenth century.
The most significant contribution to a new aesthetics
will be provided not by art historians, but by modern
social psychologists. The aesthetics of the past

legislated on philosophical grounds; what must be
done now is to *discover* the laws of aesthetics by
analyzing the new man.

⊙

There will be *new* arts of which we have only the
barest intimations as yet, but for which technology has
already supplied the basis. Joris Karl Huysmans was
the first to conceive the idea of a "scent organ,"
later taken up in a satiric vein by Aldous Huxley,
who further predicted the "feelies" as the next step
after the "talkies." The "Structures sonores"
with which the French composer Jacques Lasry
operates, have begun to open up realms of tonality
which, because of the limitations of the human ear,
have never thus far been heard. A "color music" is now
being practiced and *taught* in the United States;
fantasies that arouse new emotions are the color
symphonies which the American musical engineer,
William Herrschaft, began to perform in 1959 on
the "mobilux." The mobilux differs from instruments of
mechanical reproduction in that each piece is
played anew every time, and one performance
resembles another only to the extent that two ballet
performances based on the same choreography are
alike. It was to be expected that technology would
provide instruments of this sort; what matters is that
the range of our senses is being amplified and, still
more important, as we should all begin to realize,
that we are acquiring *new senses.*

Once when Ortega y Gasset was asked his opinion
about the relation between Toynbee and Spengler, he

*Spengler and
Toynbee*

answered: "Spengler was a genius." Indeed,
Toynbee's mind is not of the order we call genius.
Spengler as a historian had the dimensions of a
leviathan who fixes millennia with an all-seeing eye,
then swallows them whole. To pursue this image, Ortega
is a porpoise playing around the leviathan, darting
over the surface of the millennia in graceful turns,
often tossing up a glittering spray. Toynbee has
neither the leviathan's appetite nor the dolphin's grace.
A lesser whale in the sea of human history, he
sucks in, through thousands of fine barbels, a vast
quantity of food which he gulps down and slowly
digests only after it has been carefully assorted.

⊙

It is important for us to realize that we, in the
twentieth century, are concluding an era of mankind
five thousand years in length—the age of the
high cultures—and are entering upon a new era.

⊙

In his conception of the millennial high cultures—
the most important historical conception of the past—
Spengler draws a false final inference. Spengler was
inside the hothouse of the Western high cultures
and did not see that these cultures are "declining" *as
a group.* To put it still more plainly: it is not the
West that is declining; rather, the group life of the
historical high cultures is at an end.

⊙

*End of the
historical
high cultures*

The future will admit of no analogy with this group of
historical high cultures—or with any one of them;
we may speak not of a new kind of soul that will

fulfill itself in the historically molded body, but
of a new soul in a new body.

⊙

If a historical analogy is nevertheless desired,
the following is valid: We are not, as Spengler
supposed, in the situation of Rome at the beginning
of the Christian West, but in that of the year 3000
before Christ. We open our eyes like prehistoric man,
we see a world totally new, and feel within ourselves
the potentiality of enormous deeds.

⊙

Philosophers tended to build systems of thought,
as though they were building cathedrals. This
predilection has always been crippling. We melt into
insignificance beneath the high arching domes wrought
by the philosophers. Amid dismal landscapes the
cathedrals were erected, intended for all eternity,
and yet they are in ruins already. One can only view
them historically, which in this case means romantically.
Besides, these edifices had windows through which no
one could see.

◎

Attempts were made at an early date to provide   *The fourth*
mental aids for those who were trying to grasp the   *dimension*
new scientific world view. Particularly the fourth
dimension, which defied effective description, attracted
men's minds long before Einstein. E. B. Abbot's
Flatland: the Story of a Square, appeared as early
as 1884; and to this day people cite the example

of a two-dimensional "bedbug on a smooth globe," whose inability to conceive a third dimension is intended to reconcile us with our own inability to conceive a fourth dimension.

Such mental aids are inadequate because they were invented in the hothouse of the historical high cultures.

⊙

Though for the moment I shall not discuss the reasons for it, I note at this point that the world presents itself to us under a new *angle of refraction*. But our minds are subject to inertia, like the retina of the eye, which retains an image after the reality has changed.

⊙

Dimension as attribute of an "environment"

The new angle of refraction springs from a change in our experience, a fact which, since Uexküll's work on natural environment, is no longer unintelligible. Nietzsche took a similar view when he said that it was hard enough for a man to realize that an insect or a bird perceives a world entirely different from that of man, and that the question as to which of the two perceptions of the world is the truer one is quite meaningless, for to answer it one would have to apply an *absolute standard* of true perception, that is, *a standard which does not exist.*

⊙

This was demonstrated by the philosopher who, out of his desire for knowledge, decided to live submerged in water, forgetting that he belonged to a species that breathes with its lungs.

⊙

22

It is evident that the new rationalism, which no
longer looks upon those phenomena of our time that
cannot yet be rationally understood as *obstacles,*
but *regards them as objects,* must turn its attention to
a number of phenomena of mental life which an older
rationalism regarded as dark delusions. "To regard
as an object" means more than "to observe." There is
no need to take seriously the works of parapsychology
thus far produced. But there is no doubt that modern
experimental psychology is engaged in opening up
a few windows through which startling vistas will be
seen.

⊙

The problems of experimental psychology *also*
call for a recognition of the new *angle of refraction*
from which we see the phenomena of our world.
—With this new perspective, the rationalist understands
that the abstract mathematical concepts of a fourth
dimension and of the new space-time relationships
have become accessible to the *senses* and thereby
entered the realm of *experience.* This new experience
results from the exploration of large spaces. The first
traveler in cosmic space will leave three-dimensional
space behind him; he will *look back* upon it.

*The dimen-
sions and the
senses*

⊙

The first trip into cosmic space will change the *mind*
of man. Even the early aviators had begun to be a
special type of man; Antoine de Saint-Exupéry has
sharply outlined the aviator type for us, though in a
romantic light.

⊙

The conception of "finite" space—quite apart from
the problem of the "outside"—presupposes a new

sense-orientation. Here any analogy can only be a *pons asinorum*. Our sons will not have the slightest difficulty with this *reorientation* of the senses. For them, a more than three-dimensional space will not only be *conceivable*, but will have become a *sensory experience*.

This is still denied by numerous mathematicians, who join R. W. Weizenböck in saying: "This breakdown (of the world into space and time) will govern any picture we can form of the world as long as our sense organs retain their present structure."

But this is precisely the kind of structural change that confronts us now: the second psychosomatic metamorphosis of man at the end-stage of the traditional high cultures.

⊙

It should be noted, moreover, that four-dimensional bodies have long been represented graphically, and that such representations are just as clear to a mathematician trained in four-dimensional thinking as a perspective drawing of a cube is to any schoolboy.

There is no longer anything startling about Poincaré's statement that "If a man devotes his whole life to four-dimensional geometry, he may succeed in forming a mental image of a four-dimensional body."

⊙

To my knowledge, only C. S. Lewis (in his novel *Out of the Silent Planet*) has thus far succeeded in presenting the possible existence of spiritual beings in a light which modern physicists can no longer dismiss as insane. (He calls them "Eldilas"; the Anglican Christian in Lewis cannot help inventing a few gods.)

Nowadays matter is transformed into energy and

back again into matter; objects can be removed from a
sealed container without harm to the container;
modern physicists, in short, can perform tricks for
which they would formerly have been burned at the
stake. Such tricks appear in a new light when the
cyberneticians tell us that, though certain technical
difficulties have not yet been surmounted, it is within
the realm of theoretical possibility to "telegraph a man"
(that is, to break down the formula of a man into its
parts, to transmit them, and to recompose them
elsewhere without destroying the organism).

⊙

There is still a fatal tendency to look on such   *The blood*
institutions as the "blood bank" (in which human   *bank*
blood, classified by "groups," is stored, ready to be
used for transfusions) and the more recent "eye bank"
through the eyes of Edgar Allan Poe, that is, to see
them with a shudder. Yet today man's lifesap is a
well-known *tinctura composita* and no longer a
mysterious elixir; it is quite uncontemporary to
shudder at the idea of its being kept in the refrigerator.

⊙

This brings us to the field of surgical experimentation,
described by H. G. Wells in 1896, in *The Island of
Dr. Moreau.* Less on surgical grounds than for purely
humane reasons, Wells makes Moreau fail. But today
we can accept neither of the two motivations of this
failure.

Banks for arms and legs, collected at the scenes of
accidents, to be utilized in connection with other
accidents, will be a commonplace for our children.
Strange as it may sound, medical men whose
professional knowledge leads them to regard such a

development as impossible, should be told that predictions of this kind are beyond their scope. Their business is the next step, not the prediction of the step after next, which is the province of observers who draw inferences from general trends. But in our special case the next technical step has already been taken: with the device for suturing blood vessels, developed by W. P. Demichow. Here, incidentally, we have an example of how needs and techniques promote one another. Technically, this device might have been constructed much sooner. But such inventions were not *wanted*, and there is no doubt that the opposition to them was Christian. We must begin to realize that "Christian" and "humane" are not necessarily the same thing.

"Christian" and "humane" are no longer identical

⊙

There is no doubt that Edmond About's *The Man with the Broken Ear*, an entertaining novel published in 1862, in which an officer is dehydrated for purposes of conservation, and revived by moistening, is ceasing to be utopian. Whatever the methods may be: now that not only blood and sperm but tissues and organs (chickens' hearts and dogs' kidneys) are being preserved, one can only infer that it will soon be possible to preserve human beings. There is no doubt that at this moment man has acquired a self-mastery which has *suddenly* removed him farther from the man of the historical high cultures than the latter was removed from prehistoric man.

⊙

Artificial insemination ends waste

In popular thinking, the accents are wrongly distributed. The fact that cows in Denmark can be inseminated with the refrigerated sperm of American

bulls (the waste of millions of sperm cells, occurring in
the normal sexual act, is reduced by dilution, so that a
single emission of sperm can be used to fertilize more
than thirty cows), and that today the churches as well
as our legislators are beginning to concern themselves
with the problem of artificial insemination—these are
accents more significant for our times than the
relations between Moscow and Washington.

⊙

The artificial insemination of human females (and its
widespread acceptance) is an example of how
irresistibly the new possibilities are coming to be
recognized. Theology as well as jurisprudence hobble
along with their interpretations, which before long will
seem just as absurd as the ordinance that was in force
in England not so very long ago, prescribing that
every moving automobile had to be preceded by a man
on foot, waving a red flag.

⊙

From the insemination of more than thirty cows by a
single emission of the sperm of a highly qualified bull
it is only a step, now that artificial insemination has
been accepted virtually without opposition, to a
eugenics and population policy unburdened by
Christian prejudices. It is clear that the old argument
of the eugenicists (if horses and dogs are bred
selectively, why not men?) is right, once we cease to
confuse the question with considerations of Christianity.

⊙

A step of this kind will for the first time—without
benefit of Christian ethics—draw a sharp dividing line
between sexual pleasure and reproduction. Such a
distinction seems to be a psychological necessity

Separation of sexual pleasure and reproduction

27

specific to man—to animals, desire and reproduction
are identical, because the *desire*, which leads to
reproduction, is present only briefly, in the rutting
period. A *physiological* need leading to uncontrolled
reproduction exists only in the animal world, not in the
world of man, who can control his drives. (It is
human, that is, given only to man, to control his
impulses.)

⊙

"Be fruitful and multiply"—such a commandment, like
its opposite, can result only from insight into a political
necessity, and not from insight into a task imposed by
nature.

⊙

After the discovery of the conditions under which
mutations can be induced, the *planned* production of
animals and plants with desired qualities has begun
once more to develop, after stagnating for 5,000 years.
Neither the philosophers of history nor the historians of
culture have noticed or appreciated the fact that
progress in the domestication of animals was concluded
by 2000 B.C., and that since then there have been no
new domestications. The knowledge of present-day
biologists would permit us to domesticate any animal
whatsoever. Since all plants must also be considered in
the same light, it is clear that man is compelled to
enter into a new relationship with nature.

⊙

New domes-   For the moment it looks as though the domestication
tications are   of additional animals would be useless, since any kind
to be expected of work would be performed more cheaply by
mechanical means. If, however, we extend the notion of

28

"domesticated animal" to microbes, we gain an
intimation of vast new possibilities. The shift of accent
from the "individual animal" to the "animal species"
shows how the concept has broadened. For some time
now, the individual cow "Louise" whom farmer
Schulze, Dupont, or Smith nurses through her illnesses,
has had her counterpart in the American cow "Elsie,"
who is not an individual cow (she is replaced every few
years, like the bull Apis in ancient Egypt), but a
symbol of her species, a symbol of "national milk
production"—the only appropriate way to look on the
breeding of animals in the future.

⊙

Yet the relationship between man and animal has not
been stripped of its emotional possibilities. These
are preserved in *ornamental* domestication: man retains
his affection for the parakeet at home, for the
Lippizaner horse in the Spanish Riding Academy, for
the goldfish, the greyhound, and the Siamese cat. Of
course it will be possible, by the use of "directed"
mutations, to develop hitherto unknown ornamental
forms. —No doubt some day even the axolotl may be
taught to fly.

Once it has become possible, by means of directed
mutations, to breed men of every type, this possibility
is sure to be utilized. A particular possibility is the
breeding of a type which finds contentment in menial
labor, a breed of men who might best be called "happy   *The happy*
imbeciles." Here again it will be necessary to consider   *imbeciles*
the Protean concept of "humanity" from a new angle.
Then, first of all, breeding of all kinds will come to be
regarded as a characteristic and *privilege of man*
(given to no animal); second, seen from the new angle,
the "happy imbecile," as the term itself indicates, will

29

cease to be an object of pity but, from the standpoint, for example, of those who today perform physical labor, an enviable figure in many respects. There is no need for me to develop the idea; Aldous Huxley has done so with his alpha-beta-gamma-delta types, though, being a mene-tekel utopian, he misinterpreted them.

For the present I must decline to bring up the philosophical question: to what extent will "human," as a designation of species, and "human," as an ethical quality, coincide? In its sociological aspect the question was answered more than fifty years ago by the Durkheim school, which came to the conclusion that unethical behavior in a human society is "normal" as long as it remains within certain statistical limits.

Notes
on
Technology

The history of technology begins in the nineteenth century A.D. Most "histories of technology" start out with the Chinese-Babylonian-Egyptian-Greek-Roman-Arab mechanisms of antiquity: the wheel, the door-knocker with counterweight, the movable shaving-mirror. But this is nonsense. It reveals a tendency to belittle original achievement by pointing to precursors, thus throwing a sop to one's own unoriginal ego, and also indulging the pride of the humanist in showing that the ancients had *this, too.*

Antiquity had no technology

⊙

The ancients had a certain kind of mathematics, a certain kind of physics, and a certain (al-)chemistry. In practice, this resulted in mechanics, but not in technology. Mechanics is static, technology is dynamic, a "questioning of nature under torture" (Spengler), an enslavement no longer solely of visible things, but also of the *invisible,* of energy.

⊙

For this reason, the automatons of the Baroque period cannot be classified as technological achievements. As mechanisms serving primarily as toys of the upper social groups, they belong, in cultural history, with the *homo ludens* of the late Middle Ages, and therefore with the pretechnical period of the nineteenth century.

Technological thinking is the result of a mutation

Robertson's "phantasmagorias" (beginning in 1795) have as little connection with the Lumière brothers' cinematograph (beginning in 1895) as Jacquet-Droz's (1752–91) automaton, "The Scribe," has with a modern rotary press, or the foot-cycle of Herr von Drais with a motor-cycle. There is no "gradual" development from one to the other; these things are separated by a mutation, the mutation from mechanical to technological thinking.

The very ancient and repeated invention of gunpowder is a notable curiosity. But the genuinely technological idea of controlling explosions was confined to limited territories; its revolutionary implications were understood only in connection with the art of warfare, and nowhere understood in a general sense. (Even the artillery men of the Western Renaissance still behaved like magicians.)

⊙

Misunderstandings (blind spots) of this kind are still reflected in our technological vocabulary. Thus the term "internal combustion engine" is still a product of evolutionary-mechanistic thinking, which considers a qualitatively new process (for which everyday language, in accord with our feeling, has accepted the word "explosion") as no more than a rapid accumulation of steps belonging to an older process.

Technology devours the older disciplines

"Mechanics" was a limited discipline. It took "technology" to swallow up such divergent disciplines as physics, mathematics, chemistry, and, more recently, biology, and experimental psychology.

⊙

It is with the help of his "technological" intelligence that man, for the first time in his history, has learned to enhance not only his muscular capacities but also the intensity and range of his senses. He can examine the inside of a block of steel without destroying it and view any desired point on earth without going there; he can see in dark places; techniques already available make it possible to hear the barest whisper at remote distances without using wires. We are even on the verge

34

of realizing the telepathist's dream: the direct auscultation of other people's brains.

This is decidedly more than an *extension* of our senses, such as that achieved for the sense of sight, long before the technological age, by the microscope and telescope; technology has brought about a qualitative change in the senses, given them a new power of *penetration*.

⊙

When we have succeeded in extending the short-range senses (feeling, smell, taste) in the same way, the question is bound to come up once more: what is the use of all this? It is a question befitting only such people as those who once refused to look through Galileo's telescope.

⊙

The notion that the senses of civilized man had grown blunter (the basis of comparison being an abstractly conceived "natural man") is one of those ideas that cropped up in the early stages of urbanization. A sharp contrast was seen between cityman and countryman, and in respect to the senses it was held that the cityman lost a great deal and gained nothing. Complex as these analyses sometimes were, they were all based on analogies that have meanwhile lost their meaning, as for example the observation that the cityman has lost the admirable capacity for distinguishing the footprint of a squirrel from that of a weasel.

The senses of civilized man are more highly differentiated than those of primitive man

Actually the sensitivity of civilized man has become heightened, as for example toward the weather, which may cause the urban Roman to take to his bed, while merely inspiring reflections about the harvest in the countryman from Frascati. This enhanced sensitivity has its negative effects (negative only as long as we are not yet able to air-condition entire cities): in New York, a generation is growing up that is no longer capable of working without air-conditioning. Accordingly, this generation will be provided with air-conditioning.

⊙

It is unreasonable to deplore the fact that man, in our present artificial environment, is losing his relationship with the so-called natural cycles (his dependence on day and night, winter and summer, sowing time and harvest time). If man is regarded not as a higher mammal but as *homo sapiens*, his greatest potentiality is precisely that he may cast off this dependence. To this way of thinking, to be "human" means to feel independent of a nature which is far from perfect but, quite to the contrary, needful of innumerable improvements.

⊙

In addition, civilized man requires not only a heightened sensibility, but also a highly developed organ for the evaluation of sensory stimuli, in order to make his way in the world. The crossing of Times Square or Piccadilly Circus on foot, the navigation of the Place de la Concorde in an automobile, require an extreme alertness of the senses and an ability to evaluate the sensory stimuli released by a world of fleeting signals which is certainly as complicated as the signal world of the jungle, if not more so—and at least equally dangerous.

⊙

Technology has placed us in a new *sensory* world and thus subjected us to so sudden a transformation that the interpretive intelligence has not been able to catch up. It is *not* the reverse that is true. Qualitatively, this change is more thoroughgoing than has hitherto been suspected. We must come to understand that it is a *psychosomatic* change.

⊙

This psychosomatic change which has come over us in the age of technology (and which will be concluded in the next two generations) places us in a new world of experience, where our *senses* will be able to evoke entirely different ideas of "space" and "time," for example, from those known to men of the old cultures.

Teaching the theory of relativity

The change is vividly exemplified for us by the failure of our attempts, hitherto, to make relativity comprehensible by means of mathematical demonstrations on the blackboard. Such efforts fail, not because the relativity theory is, as we thought, the product of an extravagantly *heightened* intellect, but that of an already *transformed* intellect.

"Understanding" relativity presupposes not only a rather special intelligence, but new sense perceptions. This is demonstrated by every *young* physicist or mathematician who is already *living* (not merely thinking) in the new realms of space and time, and who simply cannot understand what is supposed to make relativity so hard to "explain."

In the coming generation it will be possible to bring to average high school students a complete understanding of the theory of relativity.

⊙

Such a sudden intuitive grasp is illustrated by the rapidity with which the theory of antipodes, utterly *inconceivable* at the time of its appearance (because it contradicted sensory experience), came to be universally understood. Since Magellan, the roundness of the earth has been not only *known* but also *experienced*, so that the theory no longer requires a labored explanation (although an explanation is still necessary).

⊙

Dreams and space-time

An excellent bridge to the understanding of a new space and a new time is provided us by dreams, which to be sure are followed by an awakening, an emergence from other times and spaces.

In dreams we see more—or we see old elements combined into something new. August Kekulé saw the benzol ring in a dream; Niels Bohr is said to have seen the structure of the atom in a dream; and during his work on Egyptian hieroglyphics, Heinrich Karl Brugsch often found solutions in a dream. These achievements did not come into being through merely continuous logical thinking in our space and time.

⊙

The Monk of Heisterbach and the insane

We must also be aware of a timelessness such as we experience in a state of unconsciousness, though we can draw no profit from this experience. This is the only case in which we experience the *beginning* of a time that was not arbitrarily posited. Everyone who awakens from anaesthesia is another Monk of Heisterbach.

⊙

But the inmates of every insane asylum demonstrate the possibility of living *constantly* in other times and spaces.

⊙

Such indications and many more serve to make us aware of the relativity of space and time. However,

38

they are mere expedients which do not suffice, for example, to convey anything more than a mathematical understanding of the problem of the dilation of time during the journey (at a velocity approximating that of light) to a star that is a thousand light years away from us.

And yet the first man to travel such a distance and *experience* this problem will not be greatly surprised to learn that he has been fated to live through a thousand years of the history of that star in 7.6 travel-time years; nor that on his return after 26.4 travel-time years, he will arrive upon an earth that has meanwhile grown more than two thousand years older, so that he will be in the situation of greeting approximately the sixty-fifth generation after his own.

The fact that the technological age began in the nineteenth century is demonstrated by events that have since then become legendary: the power loom, 1785; the steam locomotive, 1829; the telegraph, 1837—three examples standing for industry, travel, and communication. The power loom, as is confirmed by its date of birth, was at first associated with the mechanical world; once it was understood to be a *technological* invention (of this I shall have more to say), it proved to be a child of the nineteenth century.

On the relationship between transportation and communication: *It was then for the first time that they could be understood to be two different things.* Up until then, transportation moved men and things and so promoted communication. The most important hallmark of the technological age was that now

The legendary achievements of technology

communication became possible *without* the moving of men and things.

But the random combination of data of all kinds is too easy and proves nothing. The dominant process is to be seen, not in isolated occurrences, but in the crystallization of available techniques into that new phenomenon which has been called the First Industrial Revolution.

This epoch of the First Industrial Revolution was outwardly characterized by a vista of smoking chimneys. The use of coal as a source of heat will strike our children as insanity.

The fact that with technology man's natural measurements ceased for the first time in history to provide the measures of all things (that suddenly a new mode of thought took over, based on energies rather than measurements) was concealed for many years by the fact that machines (in so far as they were looked upon philosophically, that is, without social resentment) were regarded merely as a quantitative but not qualitative change, a multiplication of the things (tools) which had hitherto been developed in the invariable scale of human measurements. It was said— this was an interpretation of the power loom—that the weaver no longer worked with two hands but with twenty hands at once. This corresponds to the condescending interpretation (possible only long after the fact) of early man's implements as (merely) an "extension of the hand."

To continue with the example of the loom: the inadequacy of this quantitative explanation should of course have become evident the moment "quantitative" improvement enabled the weaver to perform a "qualitatively" different function—namely to *supervise* the machine instead of *working* at it.

Thinking in terms of energies

⊙

The beginning of such a new appraisal introduced what, in an attempt to classify the headlong development of the technological age, has been called the Second Industrial Revolution. In recent years statistics have been drawn up on the subject. Over a period of 5,000 years the daily production of a brick maker was roughly 500 bricks. The First Industrial Revolution enabled a factory to produce 500,000 bricks a day per worker employed. The Second Industrial Revolution is characterized by the acquisition of new materials: it no longer increases the production of bricks, but replaces the brick with more rational building materials.

⊙

From the standpoint of the Second Industrial Revolution, the First was characterized by the waste of raw materials: I have spoken of the use of wood and coal as fuel, which will strike our grandchildren as ridiculous. The Second Industrial Revolution is engaged in wasting petroleum and natural gas; we must regard this as an intermediate phase.

On the waste of energy

In Western civilization there is an overlap in our utilization of energy (new sources of energy are opened up but the old sources are retained); in the great states of Asia the development will be revolutionary. In India, 75% of the country's needs of energy are

met by burning dried cow-dung (roughly 224
million tons, which would otherwise have been used as
fertilizer). This has already been recognized as wasteful.
From the standpoint of the nineteenth century the
forcible building of dams in the underdeveloped
countries of Asia and Africa (in so far as they are
intended primarily not as a means of preventing floods
but as sources of energy) would have been historically
correct; from the standpoint of the twentieth century,
in a day when the Amplitron has already been invented
and when the productive use of nuclear fission is
impending, dam-building has become an anachronism.

⊙

The unjustly
demonized
machine

Misinterpretation of the machine, which can be
corrected, went hand in hand with the romanticizing of
the machine begun by the poets and still current in our
daily language.

The "hand on the wheel" was felt as the hand
holding the reins. The power of engines was
measured in horse power, and at first people definitely
thought of it in terms of horses whose energy was
being "harnessed." There is a romantic element in the
combination of precision and danger peculiar to many
machines. This makes it necessary—as all the early
aviators were well aware—to be prepared for trouble
even when the machine is functioning perfectly, and to
exchange trust for watchfulness.

The demonization of the machine began early and
remained in force longer than the romantic view, which
has since been debunked by the coarse irony of the
airmen in World War II. The machine is demonized
only by those who feel helpless in its presence. Where
such demonization occurs today, its authors are neither
scientists, nor engineers, nor managers, nor workers,

but only outdistanced philosophers and writers sulking in their historical corner.

⊙

These anguished Western philosophers and writers have no right to make fun of the songs of their Russian colleagues, of hymns to "the Dialectical Principle" or to the "fervently beloved tractor." *Both* attitudes are simply behind the times.

In our technological age, man can conceive of nothing that he might not invent. A magic carpet is no longer a scientific problem, but only a problem in construction. All the pipe dreams of the old high cultures can today be made to come true, but some of them are so primitive (like the magic carpet, for example) that it is no longer worth the trouble. The pipe dreams of the men of the old high cultures appear to have been consummated in the same historical period as the old high cultures themselves.

The magic carpet is no longer a pipe dream

⊙

This applies also to the utopias of the historical high cultures, including those of a social and political character. We *cannot have the slightest idea* of the utopias and pipe dreams that will be developed by our grandchildren, who will no longer be sitting inside the hothouse of one of the historical high cultures.

To regard mechanical and technological thinking as antithetical is useful as a working hypothesis; all conceptions relating to the philosophy of history should be treated in this way and not, as is usually done, as theories to be proved or refuted.

Since hypotheses also result from the arrangement of facts, it will be necessary, in attempting to characterize the technological age, to clarify a concept which has thus far been employed with disarming naïveté by our historians of technology: the concept of the precursor. Actually the notion is very easily explained if we observe certain limits and recognize as true precursors those *who supplied the foundations*. To regard Leonardo da Vinci as a precursor of our airplane builders is nonsense; he provided no foundations at all; in his sketches of a flying machine, Leonardo was not a precursor but a utopian.

The "pre-cursors of technology"

⊙

"Laying the foundations," in reference to the technological age, should be taken both in a practical and in a theoretical sense; it begins with "modern" science, with the direct investigation of nature, with empirical inquiry, with measuring and weighing.

⊙

The "inventions" of the pretechnological age are do-it-yourself inventions, products of individual achievement. They were possible down to the First Industrial Revolution, and culminate in the accomplishment of Thomas Alva Edison. But the notion that Edison was only an individual genius, the "magician of Menlo Park," must be revised; actually he was an *organizer of inventions*—this is proved not only by his development of the carbon filament incandescent lamp but by his innovations in the production of cement.

44

Even the first atom bomb was not in any sense *invented*, but organized from existing knowledge. Quite logically, the individual inventor has become an object of caricature; an "inventor" is a man who comes up with a patent pushbutton. Language solves the problem by eradication: the words "inventor" and "invention" are going out of use.

⊙

A man of 1914 would have been quite unable to conceive of a technical "invention" that did not spring from the extraordinary genius of an individual. The notion of a "laboratory invention" would have struck him as inappropriate. In those days, moreover, an ethical value still attached to "co-operation." The new word "teamwork" has purely utilitarian implications. "Co-operation" still has an "inherent value," even independently of its object; "teamwork" is only good "for something."

The laboratory invention

We hear it said more and more frequently that there are no longer any thinkers who *by their own resources*, solely by means of their keen intellects, could make a noteworthy contribution to physics, chemistry, etc., in the manner of Leonardo and Goethe. But this applies only to our transition period and by no means to any future that we can reasonably expect.

Thus, for example, the discovery of the American physicist, Edwin H. Land, that the human eye requires a mixture of only two wave lengths of light in order to register any color (the classical Newtonian theory called for three wave lengths), was in a practical sense arrived at by pure experiment ("tinkering"), but in reality through an unbiased *new vision;* the discoverer himself describes it as the study of a "natural-image situation" in contrast to the "artificial-color situation" investigated by classical physics.

⊙

Goethe, the steam pump, and the new instinctive knowledge

Today it seems characteristic of the pretechnological era that it was then possible for *any intelligent man* to understand the achievements of mechanics when they were explained to him. It may safely be assumed that any educated contemporary of Goethe's would have understood the workings of a steam pump without difficulty. The phenomena of modern *technology*, on the other hand, are no longer readily comprehensible to an intelligent man who is not a specialist. The discrepancy between general intelligence and specialized knowledge is characteristic of our intermediate period. I have not the least doubt that our children and grandchildren will have an instinctive understanding of scientific-technological factors in their environment. For our children, learning to drive a car is no longer something requiring intellectual application, but an almost instinctive activity.

⊙

The significance of the new basic principles of construction

It is characteristic of the technological age that today for the first time in 5,000 years a few new *basic principles* of construction have been discovered. It has been little noted that even the most magnificent monuments of the older cultures were erected with the help of a very few basic mechanical devices—the French cathedrals, for example, were built with essentially the same (though slightly improved) mechanical devices as the Egyptian pyramids. And the bridges built down to the eighteenth century A.D. do not differ in basic construction from those of 1800 B.C.

46

The basic ideas are, by their nature, as stunningly simple as the ancient wheel and lever but it evidently took a "brain mutation" to hit upon them. Among the new fundamental ideas, which man was incapable of arriving at for roughly 5,000 years, although the materials were long available, are—I intentionally cite examples that have hitherto been disparaged—the wire cable (only with its help could mines be sunk to sufficient depths); the cantilever (which alone, by eliminating superfluous weight while retaining maximum carrying power, made modern steel construction possible); and the cantilevered concrete slab (which alone made it possible to develop the new architectural forms).

⊙

It is interesting to note that no honor has ever been conferred on the originators of these fundamental ideas. The existing "histories" of invention stress the inventions of apparatuses, the conglomerate inventions (such as the telephone, the phonograph, etc.). There is no doubt that a future history of technology will have to concern itself far more with the fundamental principles which, by way of contrasting them with the conglomerate inventions, I should like to call *contact inventions.* Their value does not reside in themselves (as in the case of apparatus), but in the possibilities they open up, in the *contacts* they create (steel cable, T-girder, cantilevered concrete slab).

Relation of the con-glomerate inventions to the funda-mental principle, or "contact invention"

⊙

The last step of the First Industrial Revolution was the development of the machine tool. It was begun (on a purely mechanical level) in medieval armament manufacture (the boring of cannon barrels). Up to the twentieth century all innovations were mere improvements of these crude mechanical devices. The transition was announced with the appearance of the contact regulator, with the help of which the machine, by "feeling" a model, automatically created "*forms.*" (Today the word "automatic" should be used only in reference to the last forms of the mechanical age or the first forms of technology). The electronic regulator prevalent in modern machine tools (which creates forms in response to problems or commands) operates beyond the "automatic" level, and is even subject to errors of communication long known to us in electronic computing machines.

⊙

Not long ago the idea cropped up that a machine might reproduce itself. This was achieved in part in Düsseldorf, Germany, in 1940, when a "vertical boring and turning machine" weighing 1,850 tons was constructed of two parts working one within the other. The smaller inner part was built first—it then proceeded *to make the other part.* Though none of the engineers engaged in the project may have been aware of it, the idea of a *technological germ cell,* of a continuous process of technological creation, was here at work. To what extent such a creative process differs from the process of organic creation discussed under the old high cultures, is the justified question confronting cyberneticians—a question outside the province of theologians, regardless of their affiliations.

⊙

*The reproduc-
tive machine*   The question was answered by John von Neumann, who shortly before his death drew up the plans

48

for a machine which could reproduce itself indefinitely. From parts which are supplied to it, it builds a daughter-machine which is also capable of reproducing.

⊙

In the brilliant chapter on the history of the wheel in his *Sanduhrbuch,* Ernst Jünger points to the importance of the *escapement* for the mechanical clock, an invention which to his mind surpassed that of the steam engine in originality and importance. His reason for this estimate is that the *escapement,* the crucial factor in the mechanical clock, is an authentic *invention,* while the steam engine is merely a *step forward.* This comparison conceals some decisive misunderstandings.

The mechanical clock

The clock with an escapement, which seems to have originated about 1000 A.D., is indeed one of the genuine and far-reaching inventions. As an abstract measurer of time, the mechanical clock critically influenced Western Culture in its *beginnings* (or was required by it). This form of chronometer became characteristic of Western culture and belonged to it alone. The invention, as Jünger correctly saw, lay only in the *escapement*—for clocks (sun dials and water clocks and hour glasses) had existed in all previous cultures.

The steam engine, on the other hand, was the first realization of the dynamic principle which, precisely in contrast to mechanics, constitutes the essence of technology (there is nothing dynamic about a mechanical clock, even with escapement). Technology is in no respect a necessary consequence of something that went before, for which reason ancient steam mechanisms can *not* be regarded as precursors of Watt's steam engine. This too Jünger observed, but in so

49

doing merely added to the misunderstanding. What he failed to see was that the steam-engine, like the first mechanical clock, was distinguished by a detail that was even more vital in molding the future than the *escapement:* namely, the simplest form of governor. The theory that led to the first safety valve was dynamic thinking—which is not true of the thinking that produced the *escapement.* This becomes still clearer in the ensuing invention, which may be regarded as one of the key developments of the technological age: when the simple governor became a regulating cycle or, rather, a feedback regulator. Once the principle of a *feedback regulator* was recognized, we may say that the Second Industrial Revolution had begun.

⊙

The technology of the First Industrial Revolution was a *technology of movable parts*—the experience of the mechanical age was still at work. The technology of the Second Industrial Revolution is a *technology of functioning parts.* Here the dynamic principle, which spelled the end of the mechanical age, found characteristic expression: the most difficult machines to understand are action aggregates with scarcely any movable parts. A modern transistor or an Amplitron would be more incomprehensible to a technician (mechanic) of 1800 than Watt's steam engine would have been to Hero of Alexandria.

⊙

Automan-throp replaces the automaton

The notion of the *automaton* keeps turning up nowadays in many disguises. Its evocation reflects both the religious fear of the homunculus and the economist's fear of the robot. But a true automaton

belongs to the mechanical world of the historical high
cultures and is, as a child would perfectly define it,
"something you wind up and then it moves."

Modern electronic computing machines are
mistakenly called automatons. They are not automatons
because they lack the classical hallmarks of the
automaton: they are not mechanical (clockwork)
constructions and consequently do not pertain to the
"technology of movable parts." And their work does not
consist in stereotyped repetition.

They pertain rather to the "technology of functioning
parts"; they are able to store up information, to
"remember," and to "learn" by "experience." An
appropriate word for them would be "automanthrop"
(an artificial word constructed no more barbarously
than "automobile").

The perfectly legitimate transfer of biological notions
to machines (similarities between regulation and
communication in the human nervous system) which
was first undertaken by the cyberneticians, can only be
disavowed today by theologians desirous of saving
"God's Creation." (It will not be long before we can
interchange functional parts of the human brain.)

⊙

In view of the human behavior of these electronic
computing machines—symptoms of fatigue, irritability,
mistakes—we must rid ourselves of all Hoffmannesque
conceptions, of all demonization. There is no ground
for fear. "Dr. Samuel just smiled."—These were the last
words of the first report on an electronic checker
player devised in the United States, which had
"learned" so much after the first few weeks that it
consistently beat its builder.

⊙

51

A proof of the close relationship between the biological
and the electro-technical realms was provided by an
accident: a physiologist was shown the diagram
of the control mechanism of a recently designed
apparatus that enables a blind man to read an ordinary
book by transforming letters, regardless of type or
size, into tones. He recognized it not as a technical
diagram but as a biological one, namely that of the
so-called fourth layer of the visual cortex, the layer
responsible for so-called "Gestalt" vision.

⊙

When properly interpreted, the vision of the future
formulated by the cyberneticians is disturbing only to
the sensitive souls for whom *humanitas* and the
metaphysical interpretation of being are inseparable;
today they are still to be found in the train of Husserl
and Driesch, and that is where they should stay.

⊙

The cyberneticians might benefit by looking into Hans
Vaihinger's "fictions," particularly the twenty-fifth
chapter of his *Philosophy of As If*, entitled "An
Attempt at a General Theory of Fictitious Ideas."
Vaihinger's examples are antiquated (he took them
from the world of mechanics); but his fundamental
reflections on fictions are still worth thinking about.
Vaihinger was one of the few thinkers who knew
something about mathematics in a day when numerous
philosophers thought they could draw up views of the
world without any knowledge whatever of mathematics
and physics. Here one might mention the little known
fact that Spengler arrived at his conception of
history by way of a historical approach to
mathematics—this is confirmed by the structure of

his work, which begins with the chapter: "On
the Meaning of Numbers."

⊙

From the standpoint of communication, automanthrop
is closer to man than to the classical automaton; this
applies not to its structure, which is still one-sided, but
to its accomplishment.

*Automan-
throp is
closer to man
than to the
automaton*

Its accomplishment does not consist solely in its
superior speed, but also in its ability to solve problems
which man, chained as he is to a defined space, cannot
solve by himself.

We are confronted by more and more tasks in which
the limits of time are a determining factor. With the
help of a dredge, for example, a canal (which it would
take ten years to build by manpower alone) can be
built in one year. A larger dredge can be built, which
will do the work in three months. It is obvious
that in the battle between work and time there comes
a limit beyond which it is impossible to reduce
time. The picture is made still clearer by the old
school exercise: If 10 masons require 160 work hours
to build a house, 100,000 masons would (logically)
require 58 seconds.

Such predictions are disproved by practice. In other
words, they are disproved by the calculable limits
of *communication in a defined space*.

*Communica-
tion and
space*

In so far as we are dealing with manual work (or
machine work, mechanical work pertaining to the
"technology of movable parts") the accent is not on
the concept of communication but on that of a defined
space.

The picture changes when we consider intellectual
processes in the same situation. Recently a
mathematician required one year to prepare the

mathematical foundations for a new system of optics.
When he died, two other mathematicians took his notes,
went over his calculations, and completed the
work in six months. To infer that two hundred
mathematicians would have required little more than
a day would be just as absurd as the above-cited
inference about the masons. Here again we have to do
with the limits of communication in a defined space;
but here, and this is true of all intellectual work,
the accent is not on the concept of a defined space but
on that of communication.

Automanthrop, however, knows no limit to
communication, for it works in the spaceless realm
of functions.

⊙

It is now possible to endow an electronic computer
with far more "memory" than a human brain. This in
itself, however, would not make the machine anything
more than a talking encyclopedia. But I can also—
of this the cyberneticians leave no doubt—communicate
to it *any* environment and *any* tradition.

⊙

*Possibility of
an automan-
throp with
creative
impulse*

The usual objection raised, when anyone gives the
electronic computers credit for human qualities, is that
the machine lacks the creative impulse which is
supposed to be characteristic of man alone. This is
by no means certain. There is good reason to suppose
that an intermediate solution, a machine built so as
to develop its own impulses, is in the offing.

This leads us to the foolish argument that even an
automanthrop of this kind can only work with material
that has previously been "fed" to it. But man himself
only works with what has previously been furnished

54

him; he cannot live without an *environment* (in the
Uexküllian sense), which satisfies his needs and
stimulates his action.

⊙

Even so productive an animal as the queen bee is not
"self-supporting." She "works" like a machine, is fed
and cared for like a machine, and finally scrapped
like a machine. If scientists until recently looked upon
insect colonies as an "insoluble riddle," it was
because of their mechanistic thinking with its one-sided
emphasis on causality. It is here that the
cyberneticians will find one of their most important
fields of research.

⊙

Man's environment includes not only the organic world
on which he lives, but also the many implements
invented by himself, *by* which he lives (man and tool
are inseparable). This development of implements—
which were at first very simple—culminates in the
machine. Accordingly, the machine is a part of the
civilized man's environment. This inevitably suggests
the idea that *man is a part of the machine's
environment.*

*The machine
is a part
of man's
environment*

⊙

Automanthrops by now require an extremely complex
environment; for example, a regulated climate, freedom
from shocks and vibrations, and more constant
feeding than most, if not all, organisms. Whether this
means that they are more primitive or more highly
differentiated than man is something to think about.

⊙

In general, automanthrop and man can only be
regarded today as different forms that are *related* by
way of numerous intermediate forms. An intermediate
form of this kind is suggested by the projected
creation of CYBORG. Here the raw material is a living
man, who is vastly improved by the surgical
implantation of artificial organs and control systems
(his mouth, for example, may be sealed and rendered
useless, food being taken directly into the stomach
or blood stream) and so enabled to cope with
extraterrestrial living conditions such as those
prevailing on the moon.

⊙

A process of habituation (the term is not accurate, but
we use it for want of a better one) takes place
between man and his whole technical environment with
all its switches and buttons, pedals and levers, which
we make use of to release or to halt certain effects.
The notion of habituation *has meaning only for
the time of transition, before our understanding of
technology has become instinctive.*

⊙

*St. Thomas
and the
automaton*

The story that Thomas Aquinas, when the
"automaton" of Albertus Magnus opened the door for
him and greeted him, was horror-stricken and
destroyed this "android" with a blow of his staff,
may or may not be true. Today even the most stubborn
Christian would not act in this way, and that is one
proof of how Christianity has abandoned its positions—
for St. Thomas acted from a fundamental Christian
belief.

In considering the new basic principles of construction, we must not overlook the importance of the new raw *materials*. The original raw materials such as skins, wood, and metals, as they came from the forests and the earth, were the basic materials of the historical high cultures (this applies also to the basic foodstuffs of animal and vegetable origin) which have remained essentially the same over a period of five thousand years.

What we still call synthetic materials today are, in fact, a new kind of raw materials.

⊙

The synthetic material from which some station wagon bodies are made masquerades as wood; plastic wall coverings affect a wood grain; bathroom walls still pretend to be covered with tiles; linoleum disguises itself as marble, plastic as crocodile skin, nylon as mink. Such falsifications are characteristic of every transitional period. We may say, paradoxically, that we are entering into the age of "genuine" synthetic materials, that is, of artificial materials that no longer pretend to be something else but openly display their own qualities. It is an important fact that these qualities nearly always make them *far superior to natural materials*. And instead of continuing to say, "The natural material is still the best," we shall get used to saying, "The natural material is nearly always inadequate."

⊙

The so-called synthetic materials which are today used almost exclusively for household utensils, will make possible monumental constructions of whose lightness and airiness we can scarcely conceive. It will be possible to construct a stalk of grain a thousand times its natural size, and build industrial combines which hang in mid-air and can be moved from place to place.

☉

The word "natural" is losing all meaning

Yet we can calmly wait to see all the things we shall be able to make—the most important characteristic of the synthetics industry is the *transformation* of all materials. In a world where coal can be transformed into butter and diamonds, and in which hardly a single object reveals the "natural substance" from which it is made, the word "natural" is losing not only its meaning but *its value as well*. Our environment is becoming *completely artificial*.

*Notes
on
Religion,
Metaphysics,
and
Causality*

Concepts or "basic attitudes" are seldom refuted by the ensuing generation; they are *defamed*.

"Crass materialism," "sterile relativism," "hidebound conservatism"—these are examples of such defamation in our time.

Scholars who would respond with indignation were anyone to accuse them of taking a polemical attitude (though polemics in contrast to slander is a clean weapon that it takes great skill to handle) have no scruples whatever about resorting to slander. An adjective suffices—and often it is not clear at first sight that a simple adjective has served as an instrument of slander. It is only when the adjective has become inseparable from the concept that the defamation is recognizable. But by then it has taken effect.

⊙

The atheism of the Age of Enlightenment was not refuted but defamed.

⊙

The arguments of the atheists of the Age of Enlightenment are just as sound today as they were then. Voltaire's dictum that, if God did not exist, we should have to invent him, was valid down through the nineteenth century. And Feuerbach's remark that it was not God who made men but men who made themselves a God, remains a sober historical insight.

Atheism, once the foaming crest of the wave of progress, is no longer in vogue. For the last two generations or so, it has been looked upon as backward to be an atheist. *And so it is.*

⊙

In emerging from the hothouse of the old high cultures and undergoing a change which we must come to

understand as psychosomatic, we have also left the
great religions behind us. A discussion of atheism, even
a declaration of war on Christianity, is quite

All the world
religions will
end with
Christianity

superfluous. From a global point of view—the only
kind it befits us to take, impartially applying the same
historical scale of values to the events of the Orient
as to those of the Occident, recognizing that the world
mission of Christianity (as of any other traditional
religion) is played out—we can say, for the West:
Christianity has served its purpose, Christianity may go.

☉

Clearly the men of the high cultures felt a need for
religion; when they did not band together in cult and
church, then they did so in a less rigorous metaphysics,
a need for "further inquiry" into an "essence" or a
"ground."

This need of the men of the old high cultures is
more differentiated than that of primitive man. Not
only does a cultured man take care of his health; he is
also able to appreciate the value of his illnesses—and
the methods by which the priests of the higher religions
take care of anxieties are far more subtle than the
spells of the medicine men. The metaphysical, ultimate
questions and answers which are the stock-in-trade
of the theologians and philosophers of the high
cultures are more complex than the questions and
answers of the oracles. But both sets of questions and
answers *revolve always around themselves*—in the
hothouse of each high culture.

☉

What matters is that the questions and answers of
natural science have continued to develop in the last
period of high culture, whereas the questions and
answers of the theologians and the philosophers have

62

not, in any fundamental sense. The theologians and
philosophers merely try to recapture the runaway
sciences as well as runaway man. The priests with their
churches are chasing after man.

⊙

Metaphysical needs are supposed to be *"eternally
human,"* but this has never been proved. It does seem
as though anxieties were characteristic of man. But
that anxieties can be eased by other means than
religion has always been known, and has recently been
rediscovered. Escape by means of opiates has either
been penalized or monopolized by the religions. Almost
every cult resorts to opiates of one kind or another.

⊙

The effects (or cures, even in the sense of "cure of the   *Salvation
soul" or salvation) already obtainable with drugs   by drugs*
should not be regarded as a "substitute" or "escape."
We already have drugs corresponding to Huxley's
imaginary "soma," which bring about euphoria,
freedom from pain, pleasant hallucinations. The purpose
of soma was to provide a new approach to the
elimination of anxiety and despair. Huxley's only
mistake was to assume that the *old* anxieties are eternal.

⊙

But no doubt the great religions had more to offer   *On the
man than liberation from his anxieties. "What is it that   need for
shines through me and strikes my heart without   religion*
wounding it? I freeze insofar as I am unlike it, and
I burn insofar as I am like it." This *dual relationship
to a superior power* (here quoted from St. Augustine)
is characteristic of all religions; it does not merely
exist: it is a need that rises and falls, and it is most

highly developed in the great religions. It springs from another relationship, that of man to his natural environment—a relationship that has remained almost changeless for five thousand years. If this relationship to the natural environment changes—and this is what is happening to man for the second time in five thousand years, for he has now begun to exchange his natural environment for an artificial one—it becomes highly questionable whether he will again feel the need for "a dual relationship to a superior power," whether "religion" in general will be a need of man in the future. We can only wait and see.

⊙

But in considering the great religions of the past we must bear one thing clearly in mind: the problem of the existence of God, of a creator of heaven and earth, of a *first cause,* must be dissociated from the general problem of religion. There are many religions which have *no God*—there are some three hundred million Buddhists *who have religion without having a God.*

By peering into the cultural hothouse, we are able to understand the religions; they can be explained and interpreted. The question of the origin of the world has nothing to do with them. To examine the answers of the religions from the standpoint of true-or-false is an occupation for the members of the various churches. We can only appraise and classify them according to the psychological utility they had for man.

Religion as an object of scientific inquiry

Thus religions cease to be in opposition to sciences, and become the objects of scientific inquiry.

⊙

In regard to their spiritual utility, the religions are an object of anthropology, or more especially, of

64

psychology. In regard to their social utility, they are objects of sociology. Both the psychological and the social uses of religion were enormous throughout the history of all the traditional high cultures. (It goes without saying that henceforth all metaphysics will likewise cease to be in opposition to the exact sciences, and become their *object* instead.)

To ask poker players why they follow the rules of poker would be silly; they do it because they are poker players. If they played poker according to the rules of bridge they would either be poker players gone mad or else, and this is more likely, they would be bridge players.

⊙

There are not only meaningful and meaningless questions; a great source of confusion are those questions which are formulated in a meaningless way, i.e., based on the wrong frame of reference.

An example of this would be to ask a pianist who has just struck an "A" whether his "A" is blue or green. Here, the formulation of the question is meaningless. The question itself, however, is not at all meaningless in another frame of reference supplying a higher context such as, here, synaesthesia. It even has empirical meaning, as Rimbaud could have explained when he was writing his "Voyelles."

Thought should not be too ambitious. It must know where its limit lies in each particular frame of reference. Basically, there is no merit in continuing indefinitely to ask more questions; any child can do

The validity of the question

that. The meaninglessness of perpetual questioning is made evident by the fiction of the endless "chain" of causality before and after every accident.

⊙

Theology begins the cosmological proof of the existence of God (all proofs of the existence of God are subordinated to the cosmological proof) with that pre-eminent question of all time, as to the "first cause," and *answers* the question *with* the "first cause": God.

Theologians looked benevolently on the successful efforts of classical scientists to carry the chain of causality further backward, and whenever a new answer was won, proceeded to ask the same question: "What was the cause of that?" And always their answer was: "God," though they rejected, as inadmissible, the logical counter-question: "And what caused God?"

⊙

The problem of existence as formulated in the question as to the first cause, could arise only within the frame of causal thinking. But causal thinking excludes a *first* cause; in order to posit a first cause none the less, the theologians cited the first chapter of Genesis. It is mere human frailty on the part of causal thinkers if they cannot bear to follow out the logic of their thinking, which is to set before every cause a further cause. Up until now the idea of an endless chain of causality seems to have been on the one hand a necessity to man—and at the same time intolerable to him.

⊙

Causal thinking is a "respectable fellow"

The limitations of causalism were discerned only very late—by the functionalists; *limitations*, for neither functionalist thinking nor thinking in terms of statistical truths precludes the causal thinking which deters us, for example, from holding a lighted match over an open gasoline tank. This limitation, or partial validity, was already noted by Friedrich Engels, who remarked that the commonsense which thinks only in terms of cause and effect is a "respectable fellow," but only "in the narrow realm of its own four walls."

⊙

Goethe paraphrased the idea of function as "existence conceived as in action." Mathematics gives the name of function to the relation of dependence (but not necessarily of causality) between two variable quantities. Taken together, these two definitions clarify a concept which will increasingly dominate intellectual discussion.

It has all the qualities that make for popularity; above all, ambiguity.

⊙

If we take a historical view, we see that the battle over the proofs of the existence of God was a sham battle, not started by the theologians but forced upon them by those whose conscience or intelligence led them to doubt the *Church* God and whose rationally unassailable arguments (against the *Church* God) were met with the rationally justified question as to the "first cause." Actually, theologians were never interested in "God as first cause"; they were interested in *their* God whom they called the "true God."

Only the perpetual and inadmissible amalgam of these two questions (the question of the "first cause" and the question of the "true God") prevented science from getting on with its business by way of the question of the "true God"; in all this, science showed

tact, wisdom, and humility—and still another
unecclesiastical quality: tolerance.

⊙

Nietzsche's
"doing-
doing"

In connection with the questions of causality, we might
suggest a new interpretation of the thirteenth
fragment of Nietzsche's *Genealogy of Morals:* "And
just exactly as the people separate the lightning from
its flash, and interpret the latter as a thing done, as
the working of a subject which is called lightning, so
also does the popular morality separate strength from
the expression of strength, as though behind the strong
man there existed some indifferent neutral *substratum*,
which enjoyed a *caprice and option* as to whether
or not it should express strength. But there is no such
substratum, there is no 'being' behind doing,
working, becoming; 'the doer' is a mere appanage
to the action. The action is everything. In point of fact,
the people duplicate the doing, when they make the
lightning lighten, that is a 'doing-doing'; they make
the same phenomenon first a cause, and then, secondly,
the effect of that cause."

Nietzsche makes this observation in a reflection on
strength and weakness; if I quote it in another context,
it is because to do so shows the greatness of this
thinker who can be read from different perspectives.

The quotation becomes still more timely when we
add the following: "The scientists fail to improve
matters when they say, 'Force moves, force causes,'
and so on. Our whole science is still . . . a dupe of the
tricks of language, and has never succeeded in getting
rid of that superstitious changeling, 'the subject' . . ."

⊙

Actually the natural sciences held so fast to causal
thinking that they advanced causal (pseudo-causal or

finalistic) explanations, even where a proper
formulation of the problem could in itself have
forestalled such an absurdity. For many years zoologists
answered the question as to why the giraffe had so
long a neck by saying: "So that it can reach the leaves
on the trees." When I was a schoolboy, this answer
made me think of another question: Why can a
flea jump so high? According to the same logic, the
correct answer, though it brought me no credit, is: "So
it can jump from a lady's knee into her bodice."

Finalistic thinking is not contrary to causalism, but
is one of its consequences. The mixture of teleology
and causality in everyday language is indicated by a
sign that I saw in 1959 outside the cage of the striped
hyena in the Frankfurt zoo: "The slanting line of the
back *is the consequence* of an overdeveloped
forequarter."

◎

We know that as man grows older, he increases his
faculty of combining in himself rational and irrational
elements. The most unproductive consequence of
this faculty in Western man has been wisdom. (The
aging Knut Hamsun is said to have cried out: "May I
never grow wise!")

⊙

The fact that several atomic physicists have come out   *Physicists*
publicly for Christianity tells us nothing whatever   *and*
about the value or worthlessness of Christianity; it   *Christianity*
merely tells us something about the character of these
atomic physicists, and about their fears and doubts.

⊙

69

When a scientist like Max Born "rejects" all future
plans for space travel and a sociologist like
D. Alexander Rüstow rejects all use of atomic energy,
this tells us nothing about their qualifications as
scientists, but a good deal about their moral condition.
From a historical point of view, to be sure, they show
themselves to be Don Quixotes; but purely comical
ones, for the component that made the original knight
a tragic figure is lacking.

⊙

In the case of those great medical men of our day who
profess Christianity, the characterological basis of
such an attitude becomes particularly clear, for
medicine from the very outset has been an assault on
the divine Plan, particularly since medicine began to
eradicate the great plagues which had been known
as the "scourges of God." Jesus is no argument to the
contrary, for he was not a healer but a wonder-worker.
And the Church, quite consistently, has never termed
St. Vincent de Paul a healer, but always a consoler.

⊙

The assault of It has often been observed that anatomy based on the
medicine on dissection of human bodies—which, with the
Christianity appearance in 1543 of Vesalius' *De humani corporis
fabrica,* a magnificent work which can still be
read with aesthetic pleasure, became the unquestioned
foundation of medical science—was one of the decisive
attacks on specifically Christian thinking. Vivisection
and experiments on human beings then become a
necessary consequence of a *permanent scientific
undermining* of Christian ethics and morality.

⊙

70

Experiments on human beings are particularly contrary
to the humanitarian rules of the game. But since we
ask men condemned to death to give their eyes or
limbs "for good ends" and no one has the slightest
misgivings about preparing a group of men to be shot
off into space "for good ends," the question of free
will or coercion—which remains an important one for
us—is more and more losing its edge; the nature of the
problem was made clear for the first time with the
introduction of compulsory vaccination.

⊙

The dog and mouse that were sacrificed in the first
space rockets still came in for worldwide sympathy. The
pilots being prepared for the first manned space ships
arouse no sympathy, but only *interest*. To insist on
the voluntary character of their action is to slip out
through a moral backdoor. In the last two world wars
the cry: "Volunteers, step forward" was no more than
a bad joke. Every officer who calls for volunteers is
trying to evade a responsibility.

◎

In the restricted sense, ratio means "reckoning" and
in an extended sense, "rational thinking." To judge by
its root, the word rationalism has been corrupted
(more especially in Continental philosophy than in
Anglo-Saxon philosophy), for at present it connotes
derivations from reason rather than *explanations by
means* of reason.

*Rationalism
and
empiricism*

Thus empiricism came into conflict with rationalism.
But we must try to see that it is a necessary component

of rationalism. Once this is done, rationalism proves
to be the best possible attitude of the human mind in
the face of experience.

⊙

The world of experience is increasing enormously in
scope (an expansion paralleled by that of our senses).
That certain privileged individuals have always been
favored with a larger world of experience has
been proved by the poets, for example, who *experienced*
colors as tones. The German poet, Georg Trakl, felt
the sky as a disc of lead and walked stooped over
beneath a ceiling of clouds. Similar perceptions are
suggested in such commonplace metaphors as the
"biting cold," the "lashing wind," and the "luminous
idea."

◎

Cosmogonies Most creation myths describe not what we should call a
without beginning, but rather a birth *out of something,* out
God of a primordial sea, a great darkness, or out of men or
animals. In one Indian cosmogony the great cosmic
egg arose from the primordial sea and broke into two
halves that became heaven and earth. According to a
Melanesian myth, the first human pair hatched out
of two snipe's eggs. In various Indonesian legends, the
first ancestor is a crocodile, a white ape, or a
dolphin. The utmost respect is due to the Irish druids,
who regarded *themselves* as the creators of heaven and
earth. For our own primitive feeling in these matters,
the least acceptable version is that of the Samoan
legend, according to which men developed from
maggots.

⊙

The recent controversy between astronomers supporting the expansion theory of the universe and those leaning toward the steady-state theory has been settled only temporarily, through the acceptance by both sides of an "original cosmological quantum." The still unsettled difference is between belief in a *unique* act of creation and belief in a continuous act of creation (which might still be in progress today).

Unique or continuous creation

The unique act of creation, here in the form of a creative splitting of the quantum, is clearly a traditional theological solution appropriate to the historical high cultures. It may be assumed that the physicists of the future will decide for the steady-state theory.

An excellent test.

The possibility of non-Euclidean geometries was suspected only at a late date and not demonstrated until the nineteenth century. The possibility of "other special theories of relativity" was recognized very quickly and is already being proved. From this fact we may draw a number of inferences for the philosophy of culture.

◎

Social progress since 1848 has been made without the help of Christianity, and above all without the help of the Church; the principle of Christian charity is to conserve, not change the old order. Christianity and the Church have had equally little to do with the humanization of social life. In all fairness it must be said that relapses into inhumanity have also taken place without the help of Christianity.

73

The celebration of a high office at St. Peter's is more
and more taking on the character of folk ritual. It
is quite appropriate that the Vatican should be starred
in Baedeker as a tourist attraction.

⊙

A bookkeeper who put passion into the drawing up of a
balance sheet would seem to be overdoing it.
Nietzsche was still at war with Christianity; now that
the balance sheet of Christianity has been drawn up,
Nietzsche's passion seems out of place.

◎

*Civilization
is spreading
without
Christianity*

Since the beginning of the age of technology, Western
civilization has been spreading all over the globe. It
has not taken Christianity along on its travels.
   The reason for this, it is said, is that nowadays the
peoples are able to accept what they like and what
is useful to them; and so they accept only the
technological aspect of civilization. This is not true.
They also accept abstract painting, and not only the
technical achievements but also the forms of modern
architecture, not to speak of modern music and
modern literature.
   Western civilization is adopted as a unit. Not only
do its machines encircle the globe, but its spirit does as
well. If, therefore, not even vestiges of Christianity
are adopted, it means *that Christianity is dead.*

⊙

The unity of Western civilization without Christianity
is so strong that, where Western civilization is adopted,

74

it leaves no room for any other religion. Those who
adopt it destroy their old religious world. This
means that the other religions are dying *with*
Christianity.

*On Forms,
on "Art,"
and on
Metaphysical
Infusion*

All attempts to define "art" have failed (or have been short-lived), because art is not a definable thing in itself but a function. The value of functions is determined solely by their effect, as in the case of electricity, for example. Electricity is not defined but described as a function, its value being expressed in terms of relations, the relation between voltage and amperage for example.

⊙

In the West, attempts to define art have run into particular difficulty ever since the Renaissance when, with the discovery of man as a unique individual, a special metaphysical personality came to be attached to an artist's works. As works of "genius," they seemed to partake of a special substance which could no longer be apprehended by the clear concepts of ability or mastery.

Thus the artist acquired a status above and beyond his work. But the emotional state of a creative master— seething with passion or cold as ice—should be considered irrelevant, as it was before the Renaissance and in other times and cultures. In the nineteenth and twentieth century, however, the biography of the masters became a part of the impact of the work— looking at the paintings of Van Gogh, we become involved in the painter's mad life.

⊙

The adversaries of "abstract art" have quite logically derived their arguments from the elements that have been lost; they have listed all the elements which, according to post-Renaissance standards, were indispensable for authentic art, and demonstrated that such a "loss of center" meant the loss of art

The "loss of the center" is bearable

altogether. This argument is sound, in so far as "art"
with the metaphysical burden which only the
post-Renaissance period had imposed on it, has indeed
come to an end; the men who have already emerged
from the hothouse of the high cultures are no longer
willing to burden art in this way. The metaphysical
burden of art is an invention of the post-Renaissance,
which was secularized by the nineteenth century. It is a
characteristic of the late period of the high cultures
and will pass away with them like their religions.

⊙

When I say that the argumentation of these adversaries
of "abstract art" is sound, I mean this in a sense
which its proponents would never accept. Their mistake
is to regard the artistic conception of the
post-Renaissance as "eternal" and "authentic." The
loss of this "eternal" and "authentic" conception
is perfectly bearable. "Abstract art" should not be
judged by what has supposedly been "lost," but by the
fact that in it art—or better still, form—has gained
a new function.

⊙

*The false
orientation
of "abstract
artists"*

It will be looked upon as a curiosity of our transitional
period that even now, in the middle of our century,
the proponents of modern "abstract art," far from
concerning themselves with the new functions of their
"arts," are desperately striving to inject new
metaphysical meanings into their work, though
metaphysical meaning was appropriate only to the art
of the past (seen from the standpoint of the nineteenth
century). I am referring to the absurd attempts to
interpret "abstract" paintings as easel paintings in the
old style, to the "connoisseurs" who sagely nod their

80

heads and discover in these "pictures" a unique artistic value. But the whole notion of "unique artistic value" has grown completely meaningless.

⊙

The "abstract" artist must stop regarding himself as a unique vessel of "deeper" meanings.

◎

We must regard with absolute distrust all arguments that begin with the words "From time immemorial . . . ," and resort to the hideous word "incontrovertible" and the phrase "eternal values." There is no "time immemorial," nothing is "incontrovertible" and there are no "eternal values."

○   The only objective value of a work of "art" is its effect, which is historically conditioned and limited. There are few works of art whose "effect-value" has endured over a period of centuries. The effect-value of certain works was not even noticeable to their contemporaries; it was discovered only later; Rembrandt painted three hundred years ago, but it is only within the last eighty years that he was discovered to be an "eternal" artist; and already the Rembrandt cult that was at its height thirty years ago has appreciably diminished on the international art market. As late as 1883, Jakob Burckhardt made the following observation in a lecture: "We must not let the connoisseurs drive us into the present Rembrandt cult . . . Rembrandt repels all simple people. In the uncorrupted mind there is an innate ideality which need not capitulate to ugliness because it is presented with genius." It seems likely that the evaluation of a painter so decidedly original as Van Gogh will sink rapidly even within the next decade.

⊙

Loss and recovery of perspective

On the question of *losses:* how quickly a centuries-old convention can be shelved without regret (although a supreme metaphysical significance was formerly attributed to it) is shown by the history of linear perspective which since Brunelleschi and Masaccio, since Alberti and most particularly Jan van Eyck, had become "indispensable" (Luini: "A painter without perspective is like a scholar without grammar."). The first "loss" was accepted by the impressionists who were able to see and paint interiors and landscapes in a subjective perspective. The expressionists no longer recognized any perspective at all. For our "abstract" painters the very problem of perspective has ceased to exist, except where it is employed decoratively for purposes of illusion—and then it regains its legitimacy.

The creators of culture are only rarely identical with those who *have* and *sustain* culture. Particularly when we consider the history of painting in the last hundred years, such an identity becomes so rare that we are justified in speaking of a creator as not essentially a carrier of culture but, as in his own day, a destroyer of culture. Many significant creators had no personal culture and—from the bohemian to the beatnik—even boasted of the fact. Here we have a rebellion of the originals against a society—a rebellion such as would have been incomprehensible to the greater originals of

82

the Renaissance (who were conscious of performing
a definite function in a definite society).

⊙

It is no paradox; the possessors of culture (who in
the Western countries are still largely identical
with possessors as such) can, because they live by a
tradition, get along for a whole century without creators
of culture. But a creator of culture is lost without
those who have and sustain culture. He must
subordinate his originality to them—if he is to regain
an authentic function and no longer be a burden
to himself.

◎

In the mind of the average man, the notion of
"painting," which formerly embraced a wide variety of
techniques, has inadmissibly narrowed down to
easel painting. When we are asked to attend an
exhibition of painting, we expect to see easel paintings,
unless something else is expressly mentioned.
An easel painting requires a frame, and most
people are still rather taken aback when told that a
frame is superfluous, if not disadvantageous.

⊙

But as a matter of fact, the idea of the frame has in
recent times been attacked from many sides.
One of Bertolt Brecht's main aims in his plays was to
break with the picture-frame stage. Wide-screen
projection and especially cinerama shatters the frame of
the motion picture screen. Modern architects shatter the
window frame by opening up walls.

*The shatter-
ing of the
frame*

These tendencies have often been identified with "atomization," a progressive destruction of materials and forms, and this is just what has been happening in painting since the impressionists. But particularly in painting the most important consequence has not been recognized: Modern abstract painters who have destroyed almost everything have forgotten *to destroy the frame.*

⊙

The frame was inseparable from the picture as long as the picture had the definite function of being *hung on the wall* as a memento (portrait) or as an ornament (landscape, still life), and specifically on the walls of the prosperous. But since then houses, walls, and above all the people who live in them, have changed. The easel painting had a place on the walls of our grandfathers; it has none on ours, and certainly not on those of our children.

⊙

Art collectors and stamp collectors

In this connection, something must be said about the "art" collector—a strange phenomenon that, for the time being, still exists. The art collector, hitherto regarded with respect, is becoming more and more comical from year to year. He pays no more attention to the original function of his items than a stamp collector, who prizes a stamp not for its original function (transportation), but for reasons more or less arbitrary: nationality, first printing, pictorial series, etc. The collector's activity—and this is of decisive importance—never aims at quality (value as "art") but only at *completeness.*

⊙

84

Recently I read an announcement by the director of a
German museum, according to which the museum
had decided to complete its Max Beckmann collection
and wished to acquire all of the artist's work
not yet in its possession. In other words, the museum
no longer collected masterpieces (quality) but
made quantity its dubious goal. Today, in the year
1961, it is still difficult to tell a museum director of
this kind that he has become much like a stamp
collector. Even a Rembrandt collector collects, not "art"
values, but "Rembrandts."

⊙

Most of our modern painters, insofar as they insist
on being individual "artists," are compelled to
paint for museums, since there are no patrons in the
old sense today. Yet it must be clear that a museum
which purchases pictures by modern painters (a
discreet way of subsidizing these painters) is betraying
its original function, in fact, its only proper function:
to store the testimony of the past.

⊙

Of course it might be said that in the course of their
development the museums have extended their task.
This is right only if we understand the development
as a change of function. The special class of
society which formerly gave commissions and
purchased paintings (the "consumers" of art) have,
by building public museums, cast off all their
personal obligations: not only the obligation to
commission works of art (which requires
self-assurance) and to subsidize artists directly (which
requires capital, or wealth) but also the obligation
to exercise taste (which requires education).

*Art for the
museum*

85

A stratum of society which formerly fostered art
because it understood art, has now appointed
responsible representatives, the museum officials, in
order to escape from responsibility.

⊙

In the Guggenheim Museum in New York, which was
planned by Frank Lloyd Wright (no one who has
seen the building will feel that the name, "museum,"
fits), all the pictures are hung *without frames,*
not *on* the wall but *near* the wall. Clearly their "art"
value is reduced while their decoration value in
the given *space* is increased. However, there is no
attempt to arrive at a new function, for the building is
merely the *divertissement* of a prima donna architect.

⊙

The basically decorative function of modern
abstract painting was never disclosed more plainly
than in the title of a picture by Hans Arp:
"Objects arranged according to a law of chance."
However, the program set forth in this title is
rather an abandonment of the artistic principles of
easel painting than an application of the new principles
of decoration, whose aesthetics has not yet been
explored.

⊙

Apropos of Alexander Calder's "mobiles" and
"stabiles" and of Richard Lippold's "constructions":
Calder's smaller works have an element of playfulness,
what Wilhelm Worringer calls "happiness function."
Lippold's great, magical forms carry with them the
image of the space in which they belong. However,

86

Calder's gigantic arrangement of mobiles
"decorating" the ceiling of the auditorium at the
University of Caracas combines the "happiness
function" with a genuine function in space: There, the
moving plastic forms simultaneously cushion sound
and act as lighting fixtures.

⊙

The droll moderns, who go in for painting their
national flag or a black wall as a prank, do not suspect
that in so doing they are admirably performing
their true function. Both the flag and the black wall
have a decorative value in the right place. It
remains to be seen whether these clever fellows, if
asked for better ideas, will be able to create a
corresponding decorative value of their own (and there
is no need for them to be geniuses, they need merely
show themselves to be masters).

⊙

It is obvious that the decorative function of any
painting is more closely related to the "environment"
than a framed easel painting can ever be to the
modern "wall." Abstract paintings, fenced in by
frames, are today nothing more than snobbish wall
decoration; new "art" (new painted form) is a part of
the wall itself.—And yet it cannot be denied that
the owners of private houses who pride themselves on
their understanding of modern art have a certain
instinct. As a rule they choose the bar corner as the
place in which to hang their pictures. It is also
significant that, in the construction of such private
homes, the interior decorator usually offers to provide
for the proper "wall decoration" (pictures). And
indeed this is a part of his function: to decorate.

It is the architect who "commissions" abstract painting

I must repeat that the "decorative function"
carries no pejorative implication.

⊙

To my knowledge, no one has ever stopped to think
that new aesthetic standards might be derived from
the decorative aspect of heraldry and the blazon
maker's technique of abstracting from natural forms,
centuries before the inception of abstract painting.
We find blue, silver, and red eagles (five hundred
years before Franz Marc's *Blue Horses*); we find the
silver elephants of the Counts of Helfenstein, not to
mention the Hessian lion divided into nine parts
of red and silver; the Bourbon fleur-de-lys bears little
resemblance to the flower of the same name.

⊙

It is interesting to note that Georges Braque,
first a fauvist, then a cubist, was the inventor of the
camouflage painting of battleships. (He started
out as a student of decorative art.)

◎

The black rectangle on a white circle which Casimir
Malevich submitted to an exhibition in 1913 was
rightly said to have administered the *coup de grâce* to
traditional painting, but was never really accepted
as such, even though Malevich himself wrote:
"Painting has long been obsolete and the painter is a
prejudice of the past." In the same category we
may consider the "ready-mades" of Marcel Duchamp,
who in 1914 placed an ordinary bottle-drier on a
pedestal, and by merely "alienating" it (as we say

today under the influence of Brecht), that is,
by removing it from its customary environment and
sending it to an art gallery, transformed it
into a work of "art."

⊙

Only the new decorative function of modern painting
makes it permissible to use all kinds of materials.
A *framed* collage by Kurt Schwitters was just as
absurd at the time as it is today. But a new
"painting" (scattering of forms) with stone, metal,
paint, textiles, pebbles, diamonds, and tinsel on an
interior or exterior wall can not only mean something
in the right place, but can give intense
aesthetic pleasure.

⊙

We are at the dawn of a multicolored world—we have
hitherto been living in a world of single colors.
The color reproduction methods of the last decades
have ushered in a new vision. Color photographs
and color films are the beginning of the new
polychrome vision. For example, we must be prepared
shortly to see color spread from the advertising
columns of our newspapers to the news sections,
where various features will be identified by color, so
that, for example, we may recognize political
commentary by its red color, a news item about the
latest affair of a popular movie star by its purple hue,
and only the obituaries well still be known by their
customary black print.

Toward a new, multi-colored world

⊙

Film historians have shown a notable lack of insight
by speaking always of color films, instead of

polychrome films. At least in its effect the black
and white film was always a color film; it was the *many*
colors, the polychrome, that first provided new
pleasures.

⊙

The polychrome world: The Italians must be
credited with the reintroduction in modern times of
polychrome architecture. It is of no importance that
the idea of the new polychrome façades should
have come from advertising men rather than architects.
The trend is deep-seated: Anyone who has observed
the aggregate effect of Manhattan skyscrapers
will be convinced that Manhattan will soon become
a polychromatic city. Colored glass and metal
provide the décor of the new skyscrapers. And here
we can only wonder: why, actually, did skyscrapers
have to be predominantly gray for more than sixty
years? Colored materials were always available.
But there was a strange reluctance to use them in
combinations.

⊙

*To print
black on
white is a
mere
convention*

It is pure convention to print black on white and to
suppose that this is the best way. Not only
typographers but above all oculists would have
suggested better possibilities long ago—if they had
been asked. Formerly, whiteness was a sign of quality
in paper, an indication of its "purity"; black ink
was favored for its durability.

Actually the legibility of a printed page depends
less on the color relation between print and background
than on generous spacing. However, the new color
possibilities—apart from legibility, a question for
the oculist—can release new aesthetic effects

90

(which must be estimated in advance by the
typographer).

⊙

The old polychrome books, known as "illuminated,"
were succeeded in the industrial age by "books
with color reproductions." The reproductions were
additions; the aim was to make the color as naturalistic
as possible. The letter-press technique developed
from the minimal three-color process to the
four, eight, and twelve-color process. This led to a
new brilliance which surpassed that of the originals.
By the strict standards of the nineteenth century, which
was attached to its originals, this was and remains
a falsification.

⊙

The polychrome printing of the future will not
derive its qualities from naturalistic ambitions. Its aim
will not be to reproduce originals faithfully. Its
possibilities lie not in the direction of "educational"
reproduction but in the realm of book decoration. The
range of such possibilities has been shown us by
children's books in which color becomes functional.
In their use of color as a decorative function
(the designers of American children's books are not
afraid of surrealist or abstract ideas) children's
books are in advance of the other departments of
book production.

⊙

The trends in book design since after World War II,
both for belletristic and scientific works, have been
perfectly predictable. There would seem to be

91

little room for surprises. But the surprises will come.
They will be provided by polychrome techniques.

*Impression-
ism was
merely the
beginning of
the end of
easel
painting*

We learn that the history of the modern plastic "arts,"
and specifically of modern painting, began with the
impressionists and continues with symbolism,
fauvism, neo-impressionism, expressionism (though by
this time cubism, futurism, and dadaism had made
their appearance; all these movements overlap),
orphism, abstract painting, pittura metafisica, tachism,
surrealism, suprematism, purism, neo-realism
(quite apart from the realism demanded by Stalin
and Hitler, called "socialist" by the one and
"race-related" by the other)—not to mention esoteric
sects and schools and the exceptional lone wolves.

The only *style* which the future will be able to
perceive in these innumerable schools can provisionally
be subsumed under the overall concept of "abstract
painting"—and of course the political realists
cannot be regarded as precursors or inspirers. But
neither can the impressionists or expressionists.

The development of the "arts" (forms) of the future
did not begin with the impressionists in France,
but in England with John Ruskin, the writer and
economist, and William Morris, the "all-round-artist,"
and above all with the painter Henry van de Velde
in Brussels.

Ruskin and Morris must be mentioned, though they
started from false premises, an anti-industrialism so
extreme that Morris refused to travel by train.
But without their intellectual preparation, Henry van de

Velde would hardly have ventured to take the
decisive step of founding his "Ateliers d'Arts
Industriels" in Brussels in 1892. The important thing is
that they looked for new *functions* in the arts
and that they no longer looked upon the arts as
independent categories at the mercy of individual
genius, but regarded them *as parts of an all-embracing
form world.*

⊙

The tendencies they initiated were carried on in
the *Jugendstil* and finally in the *Bauhaus* movement,
which first began to suspect the function that
might be performed by "abstraction."

⊙

The inclusion of abstract painting in the general
development going back to impressionism is *based on a
misunderstanding, the misunderstanding which
consists in regarding abstract painting as easel painting.*
In reality, abstract painting, from the very start,
developed side by side with impressionism-
expressionism and had nothing to do with it. Today
it is more alive and more interesting than
fifty years ago, while easel painting has lost all
vitality since the days of impressionism-expressionism
and, after exhausting various surrealist and
neo-realist by-paths, will end in a blind alley.

*"Abstract"
painting is
not easel
painting*

In this blind alley the last lights of the metaphysics of
"art" will die away.

⊙

We discern a tendency, starting with Morris and
continuing, by way of the *Jugendstil* and the *Bauhaus*,
with the modern industrial designers, to see one's
problems as parts of a larger purpose. Although the
Jugendstil, the most complex manifestation of

93

these tendencies, made the highest "artistic" claims
(in the old sense), the men of the *Bauhaus* saw
most clearly the coming *functions* and concerned
themselves very little with art or non-art (in the
old sense).

I believe that the products of the *Jugendstil* will be
the last to inspire a snobbish collectors' movement.
The works that have come into being since then,
whose makers were aware of their function
(thus far only a very small fraction of abstract art
can be placed in this category), are no more likely to
serve as collector's items than could the church art
of the pre-Renaissance and early Renaissance in
their own time.

⊙

*"Applied" art
is the legiti-
mate art of
the future*

Even before the turn of the century, three painters,
William Morris, Otto Eckmann, and Henry van de
Velde burned their "pictures" and began to look
round for new tasks; these they found in "interior
decoration." From then on their art was disparaged as
"applied art," as a "craft," and branded as
illegitimate by the guardians of eternal values. Very
soon this attitude will come, in turn, to seem
illegitimate.

⊙

Painting as function: We forget that the sharp division
between "art" and "applied art" is a very recent
invention. When *mastery* was the criterion, no such
distinction was made.

Thus there arose the makeshift concept of
"applied art," which is regarded not as "lesser
mastery," as it should be, or as "gifted dilettantism,"
but as a dangerous adversary of "art." So it came
about that the official art experts never quite knew

94

what to do with vast categories of past "art works,"
those devoted to making objects of daily use: ivory
carving, medallion-cutting, ceramics, glass-blowing,
gold-smithery, carpet-weaving.

The feeling for function has so far been lost that
today even men of taste do not hesitate to hang
the broken-off wing of a baroque angel on
their wall and call it "art."

⊙

There have been times when a portrait painter was
openly expected to idealize his subject. The
subject dominated the painter's work, which does not
mean that narrower limits were set to his mastery, as
we can easily ascertain by looking at the paintings of
Van Dyck and Velasquez. It was assumed,
in those days of great portraiture, that a painter
should take account of a patroness' desire to
look more beautiful than she really was—which did not
exclude faithful likenesses of ugly persons.

This generous view had its precedent in the early
Middle Ages, when those who died in their old
age were represented in their sarcophagus effigies
with the faces they had had at the age of thirty-three—
the age at which Christ died.

⊙

Although in accepting a commission for a portrait,
a painter submits to certain rules, he claims the
right to ignore the wishes of his employer, and if any
objection is made to his "conception," tends to
reply that his employer should have gone to a
photographer.

*The portrait
painter
and his
"conception"*

A painter of our time would be wrong to insist on his
original conception; but the reference to photography

95

is justified—portraiture is no longer the proper
task for the painting of the present and the future.

⊙

Photography is not an "art" from the standpoint of
the metaphysical conceptions of the nineteenth century.
Yet from the standpoint of mastery there has long
been an art of photography. It is equal in rank
with the modern "arts" (forms), particularly
abstract painting.

◎

*A so-called
realism*

The champions of so-called socialist realism insist so
strongly upon its being an antithesis to something,
that we look around for a "capitalist realism." Socialist
realism is, however, merely an occupation for
mediocre politicians. The so-called realism is evident
only in the details, while the hero-worship expressed in
every picture—whether of Lenin or the leader of an
Uzbek tractor team—characterizes this school as
romantic, indeed Wagnerian, and recalls the bourgeois
historical painting before the turn of the century.

⊙

Paradoxical as it may seem, it cannot be denied that
the works of "socialist realism" have a functional
value. However, the function they serve is not
"social" (which would take account of differences
of rank and the like, and would be quite acceptable), as
the socialist interpreters claim, but "political."
Consequently, in view of their enforced uniformity,
these works perform no genuine *function* as art;
they render a political *service*.

⊙

96

But further discussion of this so-called realism is
superfluous, because the progressive social
differentiation in the land of its origin will put an end
to the uniformity of the arts. The Soviet Union will
soon provide the most radical examples of abstract art.
Its producers are in the situation of the German
postwar manufacturers who, after a period of
sterile autarchy followed by the destruction of their
mills, rebuilt factories that were the newest of the new,
since they were able to take as their *starting point*
a stage of development the others had had to
struggle to attain.

One of the few artistic forms, in connection with which
the word "applied" had no pejorative sense, is
caricature. It has been looked upon too one-sidedly
as a political weapon. Actually its essential tasks
lie in the purely human sphere. In masterpieces of
caricature, the attack is always predominantly
directed against a human factor, i.e., an inhuman, or
sub-human, or merely all-too-human one.

The political implications of a caricature have only
momentary significance. When George Grosz published
his book of drawings, *The Face of the Ruling Class*,
he professed its *purpose* to be eminently political;
but the more significant *content* of these drawings is
their attack on the all-too-human.

Even an amateurish artist can draw a successful
political caricature. Indeed, this kind of caricature has
no need of "art" in the old sense, as John Heartfield

*Caricature
and morals*

97

showed in the twenties with his photomontages
(from the standpoint of the foreseeable development
of art, photomontage holds equal rank with
drawing, and is to be judged by the same standards of
mastery achieved).

⊙

A master of caricature is a *moralist*. Let it then be
said in defiance of linguistics: *Caricare necesse est.*

◎

The early industrial products were cheap in every
respect. Neither in a qualitative nor in an aesthetic
sense were the forms produced equal to the old,
organic handicraft forms, and both the snob and the
common consumer were justified in despising
such products.

Since then, industry has learned to provide goods of
a quality and an aesthetic form beyond the
possibilities of handicraft. The garment industry
offers mass-produced facsimiles of Paris designs only
a season after the Paris *haute-couture* openings,
and we live in the midst of "gorgeous merchandise"
such as was never before available to the lower income
groups. Quality goods are being forced on people, a
process extending, through the mail-order houses,
to the last backwoods village. And if we are not careful,
the demand for trash may shrink to the point
where we are faced with an *inflation of quality
goods.*

⊙

In many areas, the idea of having things made to order
has long been an absurdity. No one would think of

asking his druggist to mix him a "personal"
headache powder with mortar and pestle. We buy
one of the well-known brands, and we are safe in so
doing. Even physicians make more and more use of
mass-produced compounds, and this they can do
because they have come to see in their patients less and
less the "sick individual" and more and more the
"organism out-of-order."

Those of the "psychosomatic" school who deny the
purely objective character of an illness, overlook
the fact that from another quarter the psyche, too,
has long been defined in unambiguous categories, and
responds just as readily to mass-made drugs as an
upset stomach to sodium bicarbonate.

⊙

However, specific needs will continue to be served by
made-to-order articles, such as shoes specially built
for crippled feet. And finally the last of the artisans
will one day regain prestige by virtue of their rarity.
Such an artisan, being a specialist, a gifted "master" in
love with a certain material, a certain technique,
will once more be called an "artist"—in the sense
that he will know how to make something for
the making of which "art" is needed, something beyond
the capacity of industry and the industrial economy.

The demand for originality that causes a thing
to be individually made thus originates with the
customer, not with the "artist."

⊙

The rank of such an artist (master) will be
determined not by his originality but by his "art"-
fulness or skill, whose most important characteristic is
that it is subject to *comparison*.

*The value
of the
vertical
order*

99

Works that are considered as "strokes of genius"
are not subject to comparison, that is, they cannot be
classified vertically by rank, but only side-by-side
or successively, that is, horizontally. For example, the
painter Klee and the painter Kokoschka, the poet
Rilke and the poet Benn can only be classified
side by side or successively (horizontally)
but not one above or below the other, and none is
"better" or "worse" (as a vertical order would require).
But only a vertical order allows the presence of
definite standards to be recognized.

⊙

In other words: Within a horizontal order *interpretation*
governs, within a vertical order *evaluation* is
paramount.

⊙

In the past, we find numerous appraisals of art on
the sole basis of mastery, that is, on a vertical order—
beginning with Gottfried von Strassburg, who in his
Tristan lists the "masters" among his predecessors.
Then, from Vasari to Lessing, from Boileau to
Diderot, and even as late as Burckhardt's *Cicerone*, the
works considered are still said to be "good,"
"better," or "outstanding," and when Vasari finds
fault with a painter, it is not on the basis of any
stylistic inadequacy, but with the certainty of a man
who has criteria of workmanship.

⊙

Only where a vertical order prevailed did the idea
of artistic rivalry have any meaning, as in a
contest between masters, such as that between Leonardo

and Michelangelo when they were called upon to
compete in painting murals in the Signoria of
Florence. Unfortunately, the idea of a contest among
artists has been spoiled for us by the Meistersingers of
Nuremberg.

⊙

We have lost our feeling for mastery to such a
degree that certain realities have no more than an
anecdotal value for us. We must cast off all sorts of
preconceived ideas if we are to appreciate Van Dyck's
famous ability, much prized in his time, to paint
a portrait a day, for what it was: a sign of mastery,
achieved by great effort and by the thinking through of
ten thousand portraits. But are we able to grasp
the meaning of the anecdote about the contest
between artists in which Dürer, after his adversary
had drawn a perfect circle with one stroke,
calmly inscribed the circle's geometrical center?

⊙

Of Ghirlandaio, Vasari wrote admiringly: "Domenico
possessed so accurate an eye that, when drawing the
antiquities of Rome . . . he drew all by eye alone,
but afterward he measured what he had done
and found every part to be correct."
    And he tells how Leonardo painted a shield with a
"fearsome monster, hideous and appalling, breathing
poison and flames . . ." When Leonardo's father
entered the room he drew back, startled, and turned
to rush out. Said Leonardo: "The shield will serve its
purpose."

*"Art" as
perfection*

⊙

101

Leonardo's letter to Sforza

To this fine primitivism we cannot return.

Nevertheless, the *extreme* attitude expressed in these statements shows us clearly the *direction* we should follow. Once again let us take Leonardo as a witness, this time citing his letter to Duke Sforza (Ludovico il Moro). He offers the Duke his services, taking ten paragraphs to list his capacities, in this order: he could build light, transportable bridges; he could fashion siege machinery; he proposed to destroy any fortress "even if it is built on rock"; he could construct terrifying catapults; he had new suggestions in regard to naval warfare and could build a special kind of ship; he had constructed mines and knew how to get them noiselessly to the enemy; he had unconquerable battle wagons to offer; he could construct new cannon entirely different from the usual ones; for peacetime he could undertake to provide any kind of architecture that might be desired, and to lay water conduits.

And after assuring the Duke that he was in a position to provide sculpture in marble, bronze, or clay as desired, he adds in conclusion: "And I can do in painting whatever may be done, as well as anyone other, be he who he may be."

And Jan van Eyck speaks in the same vein when he says that he will go on working "as best I can."

⊙

Even the nineteenth century, the century of the genius-cult, has left behind statements according to which the work of art is a product of effort, not a metaphysical outpouring. That genius *is* industry is the most widely cited definition of all. In a letter, Stendhal wrote: "When I was writing *The Charterhouse,* I read two or three pages of the

102

Civil Code every morning, to strike the right, natural
tone. In our own century, Alfred Döblin said that a
novel should be constructed "like a timetable";
Gottfried Benn declared that "a poem very rarely comes
into being—a poem is made. If you subtract every
element of mood from your verses, what remains,
if anything does remain, may turn out to be a poem."
Stravinsky wrote in his memoirs: "For me as a
composer, composing is a daily chore. . . . The
layman supposes that in order to create, one
must wait for inspiration, but that is an error. . . ."
And Jean Anouilh wrote in the foreword to his
Becket, where he describes his working method:
"Inspiration is a farce that poets have invented
to give themselves importance."

But it is useless to heap up examples. The "art
experts" in their deeper wisdom will tell you every
time: "That, my dear fellow, isn't what they
meant, at all."

⊙

Supreme mastery is present when the work is made to
seem effortless. And the highest perfection is always
abbreviation, as in "The Wave" of Hokusai.

Highest perfection moves along the razor edge
between art and artifice. It is possible to regard the
numerous forms of mannerism no longer as a "decline
of art," but as "extreme mastery"—a formative
will no longer aiming at an object and certainly not at
a function, but engaged in pure self-gratification.
Rilke has taught us that self-gratification, especially
in front of a mirror, can give intense pleasure.
To be sure, it is a solitary pleasure.

There is an indissoluble connection between supreme
perfection and aesthetics. The dancer Nijinsky

and the juggler Rastelli seem, if we are to believe
their contemporaries, to have made this connection so
clear that their performances were felt to exert a
moral force.

◎

As for the aesthetics of technology, we have not gone
very far beyond Van de Velde's remarks demanding
an aesthetic hierarchy based on a *formal necessity*
that is developed from the *logic of* the purpose.
His remark on the electric light bulb is deservedly
quoted. He calls it an admirable, unprecedented
form, as beautiful in its own right as the most
beautiful form ever created by an artist.

In making this remark that seemed so revolutionary
fifty years ago, Van de Velde—as no one could
know at the time—derived his aesthetic evaluation
from tradition. All that was "revolutionary" about the
remark was that it applied traditional aesthetic
standards to an *industrial product*. The remark cannot
be developed any further, because the light bulb
belongs to an archaic stage of the industrial
revolution. The lighting systems that are coming into
use today cannot be approached with traditional
standards.

⊙

In future, "formal necessity" and "logic of purpose"
can be nothing more than ideals of workmanship.
The results, even when obtained by the strictest
economy, will not be aesthetically satisfying
as long as we cling to a light-bulb aestheticism.
It is a very different thing to look for new aesthetic
laws in the glow of ten-thousand neon tubes.

The invisible source of light which will shortly illumine
cities in such a way that a man will no longer cast a
shadow; the starry gleam of artificial satellites;
the fiery train of rockets loaded with men—all this
calls for *new* aesthetic standards.

◎

Our artists despise ornament because they regard it
as mere gingerbread.

☉

To regard the architectonic circular geometry of
Islamic art as a mere accumulation of ornament is a
misunderstanding that is still alive today—though
Van de Velde wrote half a century ago that: "Ornament
. . . is organic and refuses to be something that is
just pasted on." And he continued: ". . . ornament is
governed by the same laws as the work of the
engineer."

◎

The enjoyment of abstraction will always be
limited to the connoisseur. Only in the realm of music
have we had examples of such connoisseurship:
the connoisseur in the gallery of the Opera,
reading a *score*.
  We are developing new kinds of connoisseurship:
such as that of *reading* (with perfect understanding) a
cathedral ground plan—and even the lesser
connoisseur cannot escape the charm of these black
and white plans, though he may understand them
only on an ornamental level.

105

As we advance in this direction, it will be among our
highest aesthetic pleasures to look through the
blueprints for the construction of a bridge, to *read*
the detailed plans for a skyscraper, or to *see*
the beauty of a mathematical formula.

⊙

These pleasures will be the concern of the more finely
constituted (the term "new élite" is so politically
corrupted as to have been rendered useless).
These more finely constituted individuals will be able
to communicate with one another. They will call
out to one another in code and live in a thinner air
than the first humanists. (Only the first humanists
lived in a rarefied atmosphere, in which scholarship
embraced connoisseurship; their disciples to
this day stifle in the miasma of erudition as an end in
itself—unproductively plagiarizing and interpreting.
The early humanists *attacked;* their inheritors
conserve.

⊙

The cobbler's-   For the more finely constituted individuals, abstract
globe   painting can perform a more sublime function than
effect   mere decoration: a function of enjoyment, which
               I should like to call the cobbler's-globe effect.

⊙

In the days when shoemakers ("and poets too," to cite
Hans Sachs) did their work in basements, they
made use of a glass globe filled with water which,
hanging between the window and their work bench,
refracted and made available the daylight
and sometimes the rays of the sun. But the cobbler's
globe could also captivate the eye; the meditations

106

of some cobblers have come down to us in
literature and philosophy.

⊙

Whatever metaphysical insights there may be, all have
sprung *from the man*, never *from a thing*. No
"picture," no work of "art," not even the cobbler's
globe has ever provided a metaphysical insight.
But all of these can be catalysts which *arouse*
insights of a particular kind. It is in this sense that
I speak here of the cobbler's-globe effect.

We gain an excellent perception of the decorative
function of abstract painting in Jackson Pollock's last
drip paintings. If we are looking for a cobbler's-globe
effect, we find it in Wols. Thus far only in Wols. In
twenty years we shall surely be able to point out
better examples of this antithesis than Pollock and
Wols.

⊙

"Reproduction of an inner life": this is a very
inadequate formula for Wols's kind of abstract painting.
Even a charlatan can reproduce his inner life, and so
can a child, or a madman, and a prisoner, as Prinzhorn
showed. Wols's painting illustrates the cobbler's-globe
effect: by refracting the light it *arouses* meditation, but
it is not in any respect a metaphysical object.

Thinking and feeling were always considered different *Thinking*
functions. During the civilized periods of the high *and*
cultures they were even regarded as antithetical *feeling*
functions. They were also radically localized:
as intellect and soul, or metaphorically as head

and heart (and not only metaphorically: Van Helmont
supposed the soul to be in the stomach; Descartes
situated it in the pineal gland). Feeling was localized
in the soul, which in turn could not be localized. It was
only in the eighteenth century that the Christian
West finally suspected that the thought processes went
on in the brain.

⊙

In periods of civilization, artists take a hostile attitude
toward thought—they lay claim to a "deeper vision."
"Deeper vision" as an *antithesis* to thought—such a
notion would have been utterly incomprehensible to
Leonardo da Vinci. "Artists" of this kind have often
been compared with children and madmen (a
comparison that has not always been to their taste).
Often they set out expressly to look for "primitives"
and discovered Russian popular art or Negro sculpture,
or took the first boat for Tahiti. They felt that their
vision of the world was not determined by reason (and
even gave rational grounds for their irrationality).
Because they sought for images and not concepts, and
because they wished to express themselves in signs and
not in logical propositions, they felt (and demonstrated
on rational grounds) that their view of the world was
not determined by reason.

There is some truth in all this. But an antithesis of
this kind (only in the West has it taken so sharp a
form) is something *very new;* and it is destined to
vanish as quickly as it came.

"I believe in what I do not know; I doubt that which I
know. This is the attitude of the metaphysician." So

says Ernst Jünger, and continues: "It is the opposite
from the attitude of the positivist. He doubts what he
does not know and believes in what he knows." The
rationalist of the future will realize that to "know"
something is merely to adopt a working hypothesis.

⊙

The confusing effect of metaphysics is in its questions;
the harm it does is in its answers.

⊙

It was only when the metaphysical interpretations that
the men of the nineteenth century foisted on the
works of their contemporaries were applied to the
works of the remote past that the questionable
character of such interpretations became
really apparent. Large groups of masterpieces
simply refuse to be weighted down with
the specific metaphysics of the late Christian West—
all oriental "art," for example.

⊙

The so-called "art-historians" (Kunstwissenschaftler)
—English universities wisely have no chairs for them—
have expressed a reluctant respect for the extraordinary
forms of the Orient, but, try as they may, they have
been unable to classify them according to their own
concept of "art." Their Christian-inspired metaphysical
interpretations have proved utterly unequal to the five
hundred temples of Bhubaneswar in North India, or to
the pyramids of Giza. European art historians have
developed the standards of their discipline exclusively
from the works of the Occident, and declared a war
to the death on such men as Strzygowski who attempted
to include the art of the Orient.

*Oriental art
eludes our
metaphysics*

We can understand Chinese, Japanese, Indian art only through standards of mastery. Perfection of form, and not any injected or suspected metaphysical meaning, can provide us with an *evaluation*. And standards of mastery are also the only proper basis for evaluating the works of our own culture. Not to mention the works of our future civilization.

☉

In Greek antiquity the artist was an artisan; he was paid as such and was almost anonymous. Sculptors were despised because they did physical labor. The work was evaluated without reference to its creator.

☉

The Greek language had only *one* word for art and craft; *technē* meant both.

☉

Misinterpre-
tation of
the cave
paintings

The forcible imposition of modern Western ideas on early art has led to great misunderstandings, as in the case of prehistoric cave painting. The injection of nineteenth and twentieth century notions of "art" into these primitive abstractions from reality has caused them to be praised as a "supreme artistic achievement," as works of primitive genius. Actually the cause of all this was the astonishing accident that these painters were discovered at a time when a "return to the primitives" had come to be regarded as a "high point" in the development of painting. Raphael would have seen this painting in the correct historical light: as a primitive first (and not last) exercise.

◎

110

"Art forgery": under the theoretical magnifying
glass of the nineteenth century, this activity came to be
regarded as a crime.

The problem itself had meaning only as long as a
work of "art" was regarded as an individual
achievement, as an unique original act, a stroke of
genius. As we have said, such an attitude is very recent
and will soon pass away. (Any attempt to impute
originality to "tachist" works, to the drip paintings of
the most modern abstract artists, in which the law of
chance is incorporated in the productive process, is
absurd.)

⊙

Art forgery was never a serious problem for the early   *Forgeries*
Renaissance painters, particularly those of the
Netherlands. It was taken for granted that a master
should make copies of his "original" ("replicas" is the
art dealer's coy term for them) and the copies were
regarded as in no way inferior to the original. Art
historians have long been aware that a master often let
pupils or paid specialists execute parts of his pictures
(in the studios there were specialists in painting trees,
animals, foregrounds and backgrounds), but so far, art
critics have refused to draw any conclusions from this
fact.

⊙

On the basis of a nineteenth or twentieth century
attitude, critics have *disapproved* of this reasonable
practice, apologized for it, and minimized its
importance. To such critics mastery, one aspect of
which is the ability to organize a work of art, is nothing
—genius is everything.

⊙

111

Our view of these matters is clouded by tradition; consequently a glance at contemporary practices is illuminating.

Falsifications   For example, it is a little known fact that nowadays a motion picture seldom reaches its foreign public in its original version. I am not speaking of acts of censorship, but of changes that are often so far-reaching as to reverse the picture's whole meaning by the substitution, for example, of a happy ending for a tragic one. If the geographical distance between the country of production and the consumer country is large enough, whole new scenes may be added, as in the case of a European film of Ibsen's *Ghosts:* the version exhibited in New Delhi has an additional scene demonstrating the dangers of syphilis by Oswald's example.

The protests of the authors and directors are entirely justified by nineteenth century standards. Today we are still not free of such scruples, and thus we all agree with such protests. Yet in the light of modern developments, the protests are absurd, and the leaders of the industry meet them with the indifference they deserve. The "function" of the film has nothing whatever to do with appreciation of "an original artistic achievement."

⊙

A trend toward irresponsibility is evident in the world of music. Since the turn of the century the interpreter has been more important than the composer. The interpreter has been permitted all manner of distortion, of changes in tempo and dynamics. He has been allowed to "interpret" classical works as he pleases, though by strict nineteenth century standards all this should be branded as falsification. And the interpreters

112

are right, for they are quite in accord with the spirit of
the classical composers, who did not insist on their
original scores. Mozart intentionally left certain
passages *open*, because he could not foresee
his singers' technical abilities—the famous singer
played a more decisive role than the composer. Bach
and other masters of baroque music wrote some of their
works without worrying about what instruments should
be used to render their idea.

Today, jazz improvisation has won full sovereignty
over its "originals."

⊙

It is only in the last few years that photography has
come to be regarded as, among other things, decoration.

Photography and easel painting

Photography has taken over function after function
from painting: portraiture, documentation (it has been
almost forgotten that this used to be one of the tasks
of art, from the historical drawing or painting to
pictures of current events), wall decoration (from the
framed picture to the framed photograph). And it
has taken over still other important functions, not the
least of these being the passport picture. A drawing
by Maurisset dated 1840 shows a row of gallows: the
hanged men are artists whom photography has robbed
of their daily bread. An allegorical ceiling painting
in the Vatican by Domenico Torti (1884) shows
photography as a "low art," situated beneath the layer
of clouds on which the "true" arts sit enthroned.

Usually photography, in the course of its conquests,
has been regarded as the enemy and counterpart
of easel painting. The source of the basic
misunderstanding underlying this conflict was that a
medium equal in rank to painting (today we know that
it is in some respects superior) fell into the hands of

113

immature persons. "You press the button, we do the
rest!" This slogan of the first Kodak manufacturers
encouraged photographers to cast aside all sense
of responsibility when they "pressed the button." The
mass of camera owners discredited the new medium.

⊙

The discussions that went on for years on such
questions as: To what extent is photography a mere
copying from nature? What is the relation between the
camera eye and the subjective eye of the painter? To
what degree can a painter arrive at "reality"?—all
these discussions may be regarded as ended. Today it is
something else that concerns us.

⊙

For some time enormous decorative photographs,
sometimes covering whole walls, have been making
their appearance, chiefly at industrial exhibitions.
Photographs of such dimensions are nonobjective even
when they represent objects, and their purpose is not
decoration but demonstration. Often this is intentional,
as when the objects, discovered through a telephoto lens
or a microscopic lens, are represented as *alienated*.
When undertaken consciously, this alienation, which
Duchamp regarded as the extreme possibility of art
(an art which had thus ceased to be art), is one of the
hallmarks of abstract painting. The connection between
decorative photography and abstract painting has
hitherto been denied, and similarities have been put
down as accidental. But there can be no more question
of accident since "The New Landscape in Art and
Science" exhibition held in Washington in 1959, when
scientific photographs were juxtaposed to the works of
new painters.

⊙

Jackson Pollock's last drip paintings, the production of which was largely governed by the law of chance, are very similar to the photographic experiments in which technical (chemical) objects are made to speak for themselves (also by the law of chance).

Photographic "art" without a camera

These "pictures" (abstract forms) are produced for example by direct chemical action on a photographic plate—without the use of a camera. The use of such technical possibilities is "photography," just as Pollock's use of a drip can is "painting"—in other words, painting will not in the future be wedded to brush and pencil any more than photography (in the wider sense) will necessitate the click of a camera.

An extraordinary combination is provided by the experiments of Picasso, who in a darkened room drew figures in the air with a piece of red-hot charcoal, the figures being registered on the plate of a camera with its shutter left open. Such experiments have long ceased to be mere play.

⊙

If photography joins hands with abstract painting, all talk of "art" (in the old sense) becomes meaningless. In this connection photography is not raised to the level of art any more than painting is debased to the level of photography. Rather, this coincidence of two formal media, which is becoming more and more evident, takes place on a plane where there are no differences of rank, because both are subordinated to the same function.

115

*Notes
on
Literature
in the Most
General
Sense*

According to Goethe, to purify and at the same time
enrich the mother tongue is "the business of the
best minds." His words are clear, but they express a
nineteenth century attitude, and in the future we must
take a different view of them.

⊙

The languages of our Western high culture have been
more "enriched" in the last hundred years, by an
avalanche-like increase in vocabulary such as has not
occurred anywhere else in the past five centuries.
But "purification" in the Goethean sense is a lost cause.
Responsibility toward the spirit of the language, as
envisaged by Goethe, is vanishing as language is
perfected for the purposes of rational, scientific,
technological communication, and impoverished as a
means of emotional, poetic expression. The scarcely
perceptible shadings of our earlier language were, quite
rightly, administered by poets; the precision of their
terms was weighed emotionally, and judged good or
bad accordingly. The precision of shadings demanded
by a perfected language of technical communication will
be decided on a rational level. This is the way to the
formula.

*In becoming
a means of
"technical"
communica-
tion, language
is becoming
impoverished
as a means
of expression*

⊙

We have an intimation of this development in the first
systems of shorthand (those that can be *taught* and
learned, not the *personal* ones which are more in the
nature of secret codes). It is clear that stenography and
speed-writing foreshadowed the speed-readers whom
American training schools are already producing, with
a guaranteed gain of 200% in reading speed. If we
take into account the possibilities of the modern
dictating machines, the next necessary step would seem

to be quicker hearing. We must come to realize that quick reading is not just a matter of rapidity but also of *better, more critical, and more selective reading.* However, the importance of mere rapidity should not be underestimated. The average reader's present ability to read 250 words a minute can easily be raised to 500 and probably to several thousand words. The development of this ability is a necessity imposed by the present abundance of reading matter that cannot be ignored.

⊙

The supply of reading matter will increase now that the electronic translating machine has shown that it is possible to translate not only scientific literature, but novels and even poetry intelligibly into a foreign language. For the present, to be sure, the machine's rendition of style, of words and images, is much inferior to that of human translators, but within a few years it will not be appreciably worse.

In 1960 the machine's output was only 1,800 words a minute; this means that it can translate a book of 360 pages in one hour. But once the slight technical difficulties in the way of more rapid registration and control have been surmounted, it will be possible to increase the present rate many times over.

It may be foreseen that the translating machine will raise one more outcry among the citizens of Yesterday, who are determined at any price to uphold the primacy of human over technical ability. I repeat: we must accustom ourselves to the idea that specialized machines surpass human specialists in all fields, and *particularly in those fields which until very recently seemed inaccessible to the machine.*

For the moment the citizens of Yesterday can still

take refuge in the sense of superiority deriving from the thought that after all man created the machine and owns it—very much as a Roman of mediocre culture had his Greek slave educated and profited by his intelligence and knowledge, but went right on feeling superior to him. Since, however, the machine belongs to man's environment, whence it follows that man belongs to the machine's environment, a new, as yet unimaginable, relationship is sure to develop between man and machine.

⊙

Such subtleties as those championed by Karl Kraus, who looked upon the correct use of such little words as "yet" and "still" as the test of good style, will cease to play a part when the formula quality of language is developed. But such subtleties will long retain their importance for poets.

⊙

What will be left for the writer when our formula language is complete? Today such a question can be answered only indirectly, on the basis of certain historical considerations. Klopstock would not have been able to accept one of Gottfried Benn's "Morgue" poems as a poem. Or Ronsard, a poem by Guillaume Apollinaire. And the same goes for Edgar Allan Poe, had he been confronted with Allen Ginsberg's "Howl."

There is, indeed, no abbreviation or condensation of language that might not be struck into current coin.

⊙

Those who are not at ease with formulas are likely to respond to every formula—by nature a product of some special discipline—with the objection that it fails to encompass "the whole." But what is "the whole"? It

Language as formula

121

is the subject of arbitrary assertions, largely
determined by subjective-emotional factors, and
consequently beyond any formula that crystallizes some
objective actuality. It is absurd to criticize Einstein's
all-encompassing energy formula for saying nothing
about the *beauty* of the starry sky. The *beauty* of the
sky is a subjective experience, and as such always
an arguable matter.

⊙

All the problems raised by the relationship of language
and thought will have to be reformulated, once we have
the technical means of reading thoughts directly from
the brain. To translate the lightning-like movements
of thought into a cumbersome word-language for the
sake of communication, is a senselessly wasteful
procedure, from the technician's point of view. If
language cannot be dispensed with altogether, then the
language of formulas here becomes a *necessity*.

◎

The historians of the nineteenth century made the
important discovery, among others, that "history" is
something more than a sequence of royal biographies,
of wars, and cabinet decisions. This discovery led to the
complex notion of "cultural history," to which a
number of intellectual disciplines contributed. But not
so the historians of literature. In splendid isolation they
went on doing what political historians had been
doing a hundred years before; as though nothing
whatever had happened, they went on producing the
biographies of *writer-princes,* and described summits
of the literary scene which tell us no more about the
true events in the valleys of the literary landscape than

the three-star designations in Baedeker tell us about
the natural landscape.

⊙

For some reason impossible to determine, literary
historians consider works apart from their effects—their
field is the "written work of art." But who, if not
literary historians, should be concerned with
investigating light literature? This popular literature
exerts a moral influence (and very seldom an immoral
one, as the judges of our juvenile courts in certain
cases would have us believe). It also exerts an
aesthetic influence; it influences taste.

⊙

I recently met a professor of literature who boasted of   *The detective*
never having read a detective novel. The man is a   *novel*
disgrace to his profession.

⊙

The detective novel contributes far more to an
understanding of contemporary man than many a work
of highbrow literature. A literary discussion based only
on summit literature may serve to clarify certain
aesthetic questions; apart from that, it yields
information about literary circles, but tells us nothing
about literature in its relation to society.

⊙

The relation between "literature" and "society"
has been under discussion for more than fifty years.
At first there was merely a vague feeling that
something was wrong with it; then this vague feeling
was raised to full awareness by Marxist literary
criticism. The discussion always ended with the

123

discovery of a discrepancy between literature and
society—a discrepancy for which literature was
regularly blamed. Literature? What literature? Summit
literature was no doubt deserving of the reproach, but
not the whole complex of literature.

⊙

Astonishingly enough, the pyramid of society as a
whole (which had long been an object of study for
various sciences) was not compared with the
entire pyramid of literature, but only with summit
literature. Otherwise, these critics would have noticed
that reading matter in the most general sense has
always done its very best to satisfy *all* the needs of
society. The needs of every level of the social pyramid
are satisfied by the output of the corresponding level
of the literary pyramid.

⊙

The demand for reading matter at the lowest social
level is satisfied by a flood of magazines with their
serial novels, detective stories, so-called "true stories,"
etc. For quite some years now this group has had an
almost exact parallel in the church tracts which aim
with a remarkable and increasing sureness of touch at
the lowest level of the social pyramid. These tracts are
sold by the millions and also given away as prizes.
Both these classes of literary products have their
counterparts in the plastic arts: popular romances find
their equivalent in lawn decorations, uplifting tracts in
plaster madonnas and devotional paintings.

⊙

Who writes   If we take a complex view of this kind, always
for whom?   comparing the whole social pyramid with the whole

124

literary pyramid, the absurdity of many questions
hitherto discussed on the basis of an absolute standard
becomes apparent. One such question: for whom should
the writer of the future write? According to the
complex view of literature, the writer should transmit
at a wave-length for which, at the corresponding
level of the social pyramid, he is certain
to find the right "receiver."

One can only be amused at Jean-Paul Sartre's repeated
insistence that a modern writer who neglects to make
use of the mass media (newspaper, radio, film)
condemns himself to be read only by the bourgeoisie.
An author of Sartre's intelligence, regardless of the
medium he employs, will always be condemned to find
his "receivers" at the level of the social pyramid which
corresponds to his own level in the literary pyramid.

The hordes of writers who connect the lowest levels of
the social and literary pyramids are not interesting as
individuals. Their work never claims to be "original";
they are interchangeable, and it often happens that a
character of fiction survives two or three authors who
deal with him successively (this is a frequent
occurrence in the history of the American comic strip).

One of the main reasons why methods of complex
literary criticism should be brought to bear upon the
phenomenon of mass literature is its steadily increasing
technical perfection.

*The technical
perfection
of mass
literature*

125

In Germany, the qualitative difference between
summit literature and the mass literature at the base of
the pyramid is still striking. Not so in the Anglo-Saxon
countries where the popular novel, particularly the
detective novel, has attained such stylistic perfection
that only a connoisseur can sense the difference.
Metaphors, once prized as a hallmark of poetic talent,
are ground out in quantity by such American
mystery writers as Chandler and Hammett,
probably not because of any inner compulsion, but
because they know how.

The best of these authors of popular literature have
at their finger tips what the psychologizers of the past
centuries had to pioneer for. Today's writers, having
read not only Freud and Jung, but also Riesman
and Kinsey, paint social panoramas more accurate than
those of the laboriously plodding naturalists of the
eighties. These days, an author of summit literature is
forgiven if he conceals an inadequate knowledge of his
subject behind ingenious formulations (particularly in
Germany; much less so in the United States). But the
authors of detective stories can no longer
afford to be poorly informed.

⊙

In the field of popular literature we once again
encounter the teamwork which, though there was no
special name for it, was an accepted practice in the
days preceding the genius cult. The most striking
example from the past century is that of Dumas père,
who wrote his novels with the help of over a dozen
specialized collaborators and nevertheless succeeded in
entering the history of literature as an individual

author. Today we find numerous examples of literary
teamwork; one of them is the resourceful authors'
collective that goes by the name of Ellery Queen.
Another is Erle Stanley Gardner, who employs seven
secretaries, and in 1960 completed his hundredth book
with their assistance, thus illustrating a tendency
that will be gaining in importance.

A more significant sign is the appearance of a kind of
specialized literature which no longer bears the name
of an individual author but is frankly presented as the
work of an editorial board consisting of scientists;
this gives the material a more authoritative stamp than
the most famous individual name could provide.—
There is no question that at a time of increasing
specialization this is the right way—at least in the
technical and scientific fields.

⊙

Since in the recent past originality was manifested
chiefly in uniqueness of form (a form so original that
the slightest change of a comma could throw it off
kilter), particular attention is due to the general
dissolution of forms that we are witnessing today.
Today we film a play, we make a play out of a film, we
transform a novel into a television series. We turn a
play into a "musical"—incidentally, I have no doubt
that Bernard Shaw, unlike the devotees of "literature,"
would have been delighted with *My Fair Lady*. It is a
mistake to regard these tendencies as signs of
decadence. Actually we have regained our sovereign
power over our material. It was formerly taken for
granted that the subject is stronger than its creator; we
are merely recapturing this point of view.

Subject matter is stronger than its so-called "original" creators

⊙

127

The discerning writers who specialize in supplying
material for radio or television have already resigned
themselves to the fact that they can never achieve
an individual personality in the eyes of the public.
They have had to learn by bitter experience that
although the two thousand readers who read their first
book sometimes sufficed to give them a personality, the
five million members of their radio or television
audience merely give them an income.

⊙

Clearly, these writers face a moral problem for which
no solution is in sight: A writer who has found out that
his work gives him no public personality loses his
sense of responsibility. His specialized skill, like all
specialized skills, is for sale.

⊙

The inflation of metaphors that has made its
appearance in light literature can be countered only by
an extreme economy in the use of metaphors—an
ideal for which the *masters* of prose have always
striven—and by an attempt to recapture the quality
of simple statement. Nothing is more difficult for a
writer than to put down the simple observation: "The
sky was blue." The feeling for the monumentality of
such a statement has been lost. It takes greatness to
register a fact in such simple words. The expressionists
would have condemned such a sentence as banal, and
would have written at least: "Gigantic sky blued down"
or, more fiercely: "Blue screeched from cloud jaws."
Today every popular writer can manufacture such
explosions by the dozen. But if you write "The sky was
blue," and then try to figure out what sentences might

128

come before and after it, you will see how hard it is
to sustain simple statement.

⊙

Light literature also gives us certain notions of writing
economy that summit literature has long since lost.
The literary critics of the last decades would have
objected to entering on any discussion as to the *proper
length* of a novel. Edgar Allan Poe still had very
precise ideas on the subject: It should be possible, he
thought, to read a story in two hours. It is no
accident that the modern crime novels that appear in
book form are *all the same length.* No experienced
writer would turn out a detective novel of 1,000 or even
500 pages. The sense of economy displayed in this
connection is the sum of psychological insight and of
a superior aesthetic experience. The best literature will
be compelled to look for new aesthetic laws that are
no longer derived from the past but worked out
empirically in this age of the speed reader.

*Economy of
form*

⊙

In the summit literature of our own time, Lawrence
Durrell's *Justine* cycle is a masterpiece of economy.
A contrasting example of the most inflated
long-windedness is offered by Durrell's friend Henry
Miller.

◎

Modern literature is in an unfortunate situation because
the sciences have left it far behind.

Let us suppose that in 1900, after having written
The Weavers, The Beaver Coat, The Sunken Bell, and
Drayman Henschel, Gerhart Hauptmann, a progressive
writer in his day, had sat down to a discussion with

*The sciences
have out-
distanced
literature*

Ernst Haeckel, author of the epoch-making *History of Creation, Evolution of Man, The Riddle of the Universe,* and a progressive representative of the natural science of his day. There was no artistic, scientific, or philosophical problem that they would not have been able to discuss as equals.

Today the writers have fallen behind. Today a physicist and a poet can no longer carry on a discussion on an equal plane. The efforts of writers without the slightest understanding of twentieth century physics to drive physicists back to the ethical problems of the last century are absurd, and physicists should have the courage to reject such attacks by persons of retarded education.

The argument that it is not the writer's business to keep up with the science of his time, that he should aim exclusively at a "profound vision of man," is typical of the nineteenth century when the "knowledge of man," both as a social and an individual being, was still a matter of intuition.

◎

The tasks of literature are still as rich and varied as ever. But one function of the writer that has fallen into oblivion in the past hundred years must be revived: the transmission of knowledge.

⊙

Literature must also transmit knowledge

It is strange that the transmission of knowledge, once taken for granted as an aim of literature, is the last thing a ranking writer since 1850 has been able to concern himself with. The desire to be an "educator" has been held in low esteem.

⊙

130

So-called topical (including "popular science")
literature has the task—which it has not performed in
the slightest degree thus far—of catching up with the
runaway sciences and making use of them.

⊙

An illustration of a function lost to the individual is
provided by Zola: by personal commitment, he
discovered hitherto unknown strata of society. A
present-day writer who sallied forth alone to discover a
new stratum of society (a "class" or "psychological
group") would be behaving like a man seeking, in
1961, to invent matches.

That job has been done. Today, sociologists and
social psychologists provide more complex panoramas
of every social sector than could ever be achieved by an
individual creative writer depending on his own
research and intuition alone.

⊙

The idea that a scientific specialist should be able to
write so as to be understood by all, is sheer nonsense.
This would mean to write without presuppositions;
but for whom?

If only for reasons of economy, every scientific
publication requires abbreviations. But every scientific
publication must also communicate. Every specialist
is a scout, whose reconnaissance is useless unless it is
communicated to the infantrymen behind him.

⊙

The most unfortunate form of communication between
the scientist presenting his findings and the layman
eager for culture is so-called "popular science." The
main trouble with those who write "popular science" is
their false conception of the layman. They construct
a model of an imbecile and in speaking to him pretend

*The calamity
of "popular
science"*

131

to be exceedingly stupid. What they forget is that in the age of specialization a physicist is a layman to the student of ancient philology, who in turn is a layman to the botanist, while an electronic engineer is a layman to the physician, and a jurist is a layman to the psychologist.

The communication needed to bring literature and general intelligence back into contact with science cannot be directed from the top down—that is the task of teachers whose job it is to address themselves to imbeciles and pretend to be stupid. It must on the contrary be addressed by a specialist to a general intelligence of equal rank. The purpose of a work on physics for the general reader is not, primarily, to enlighten the scientist's old mother or his chauffeur, but to communicate a knowledge of physics to specialists in other fields.

⊙

Einstein and the "dear reader"

Scientists who are always being asked to write popular books should refuse to do so. Their time is too valuable. Making their work understandable to the public is the responsibility of the professional writer, who can do it better than the scientists in most cases. Einstein was once prevailed upon to write a "popular" exposition of his theories; he gave the manuscript to Max Planck who returned it with the words: "My good friend, you are mistaken if you think you are being popular because you write 'dear reader' on every single page."

⊙

Obviously the transmission of a general knowledge of the special sciences to scientists in other branches and to the intelligent classes of laymen is the task of writers and not of scientists; it calls for submission not to a scientific, but to a literary discipline: reality seen through a human personality.

I have discovered that Jules Michelet, the French historian, may be called the ancestor of topical literature. When his physician wished to change his linen as he lay on his deathbed in 1874, he cried out: "Linen, doctor. You are speaking of linen. Do you know what linen is? The linen of the peasants, the workers . . . linen, what a splendid thing—I should like to write a book about it!"

One day I myself made a try at topical literature. I found that the best way to explain a scientific discovery to a non-specialist is to describe the discovery as a progressive search, that is, to lead the reader over exactly the same path as the scientist himself followed, from the moment of his inspiration to the conclusion. But I also found—and here many overhasty authors have blundered—that a writer of this kind of work must be *able to dance on the tightrope of his chosen science—just to cling to it for dear life is not enough.* The production of topical literature is a craft that a master can exercise with his left hand. *But the left hand must know what the right hand knows.*

The problem of obscenity in literature first made its appearance toward the end of the nineteenth century, when popular language began to be accepted as fit for

The problem of obscenity

133

literature. In those days the Bible with its many obscene passages, was still read aloud in many families, yet at the same time it had become unthinkable for anyone to utter the word "trousers" in female company.

In our days the problem has been raised anew by Henry Miller (whose books have been condemned by the justice departments of numerous countries) and later, after World War II, by Norman Mailer and James Jones, whose military jargon, strange to say, was no longer condemned, but accepted as a kind of artistic realism. *The Naked and the Dead* and *From Here to Eternity*, which contain the largest obscene vocabulary in modern literature, became best sellers.

⊙

The muddiness of the controversy, as conducted by the government authorities, stems from the identification of obscenity with pornography. Yet the difference between them is perfectly simple: the word "obscene" refers to a vocabulary, the word "pornographic" relates to a purpose.

⊙

The express pornography that is usually circulated in limited editions among small circles of pornography lovers is more interesting from the standpoint of psychology and medicine than of literature (though it is a tradition among high-ranking French authors to produce one anonymous work of pornography; connoisseurs can reel off some choice names).

⊙

The modern problem of obscenity in literature arose only when *freedom of subject matter* was amplified by *freedom in the use of words*.

⊙

It is a waste of time to argue as to whether this freedom
in the choice of *subject matter* was ushered in by
medical men (beginning with Charcot) or by writers
(beginning with Zola). If we are agreed that the
word "obscene" relates to *vocabulary,* freedom in the
use of themes did not include obscenity. It was French
naturalism, represented by Emile Zola, which
achieved the freedom to treat all manner of themes
in literature. Soon there was nothing of which one
could not speak openly. In the twentieth century
such writers as André Gide and Jules Romains made
the ultimate use of this freedom. Gide had the courage
to profess himself a pederast (Walt Whitman and
Marcel Proust had not yet had this courage, they
merely gave themselves away—perhaps intentionally);
Jules Romains, with masterful obscurity, described
subtle erotic practices by calling them perversions,
though they are commonplaces even among teenagers
today.

⊙

After World War II, however, freedom of
subject matter was radically amplified by a freedom
in the use of words. Slang, the language of the gutter,
the jargon of thieves, whores, and soldiers, entered
into literature. This language enriched with obscenity
was not—and that is why the arguments of the
public prosecutors are absurd—arbitrarily invented by
writers but was merely registered in every stratum
of society. In other words: the slang vocabulary
rose up like fermenting yeast and caused the language
of summit literature to "rise." Such a rising is a result
of disintegration but its effect is lightness and
tastiness.

⊙

135

Obscenity in speech and writing has become
particularly common in intellectual circles since the
last World War. To say that this freedom of usage in
the upper social classes was brought about by the
freedom of subject matter proclaimed at the turn of the
century by educators and medical men is inadequate.
It does not account for the surprising freedom of
vocabulary which has increased steadily and has
already infiltrated the mass-circulation magazines of
certain countries (particularly Germany).

⊙

Thus the word "obscene" keeps shrinking. It is losing
impact to the same degree to which the obscene
vocabulary infiltrates cultivated conversation and
serious literature. It seems likely that in the not too
distant future no one will hesitate to discuss the art of
love with a roomful of casual acquaintances at
a party, resorting in the most matter-of-fact tone
to words which are still considered obscene today.

Glossary Index

Abbot, E. B., author of *Flatland: the Story of a Square* (1884), 21

About, Edmond (1828–85), French novelist and playwright, 26

"abstract art," the varieties of which elude precise definition, 79–82, 84, 87–8, 92–3, 96–7, 107, 115; "applied" art of the future, 94, 97

air-conditioning, 36

Alberti, Leone Battista (1404–72), Italian architect and scholar, one of the founders of Western theory of art and aesthetics, 82

Albertus Magnus (1193–1280), German scholar, earliest leading exponent and commentator on the works of Aristotle, 56

Amplitron, a device for wireless transmission of energy regardless of distance, developed by Raytheon Company in 1959, 42, 50

Anouilh, Jean, born in 1910, contemporary French playwright, 103

anxiety, 63

antipodes, 37

Apollinaire, Guillaume (1880–1918), French poet, 121

Aquinas, Thomas (1225–75), Italian theologian, Church father, the first to unite philosophy with theology, while conceding to philosophy a certain degree of independence of thought, 56

Since in a book of this kind both footnotes and textual explanations would be entirely inappropriate, I have provided this glossary-index, at the request of both the German and the American publisher. It will enable the reader to find again any of the Notes which might have irritated or pleased him, and provides informally, with only the immediate requirements of these Notes in mind, a few additional facts and explanations.

Archipenko, Aleksandr, born in 1887, Russian sculptor in America since 1924, 18

Arp, Hans, born in Strasbourg in 1889, painter, sculptor, and writer, 86

artificial organisms, 14

atheism, 61

atom bomb, 45

Augustine, St. (354–430), renowned early Church father. The quotation is translated from the German version, 63

Australian aborigines, 12

automanthrop, 50–61

automatons, 33, 50–1, 53–56

"axis," *see* warmth, loss of

Voltaire, François-Marie Arouet (1694–1778), French writer, poet, and leading figure of the Age of Enlightenment, 61

warmth, loss of: what Spengler sees as the transformation of culture into civilization, commonly called the loss of soul, or what Sedlmayr calls "the loss of center." Jaspers discusses this phenomenon in his "axis theory," and Alfred Weber in his concept of the transition of the Third Man to the Fourth Man, with reference to Nietzsche. Ernst Jünger has given the most acute linguistic analyses on this subject. The flaw in most of the discussions is the sentimentality which persistently registers *only* the losses, 6, 7, 10, 119

Watt, James (1736–1819), English inventor of the steam engine, 49–50

Weizenböck, R. W., 24; *see also* dimension, fourth

Wells, H. G. (1866–1946), English novelist, essayist, social critic, author of *The Time Machine* (1904) and other utopian novels showing his firm faith in reason, 12, 25

Whitman, Walt (1819–92), printer, journalist, poet, author of *Leaves of Grass* (1855), 135

Wilkins, Bishop John (1614–72), English co-founder of the Royal Society, an early, unjustly forgot-

ten utopian who prophesied not only the colonizing of the sea floor by man, but even the colonization of the moon, calculating that it would take 180 days to reach the moon. He developed ideas on the conservation of sound (the phonograph) and on long-distance communication (the telegraph). Author of *The Discovery of a World in the Moone* (1638) and other works, 13

wire cable, 47

Wols (Wolfgang Schulze, 1913–51), violinist, photographer, painter, 107

Worringer, Wilhelm, born in 1881, German art historian, author of *Abstraktion und Einfühlung* (1908, 1948), 86

Wright, Frank Lloyd (1869–1960), American architect, 86

Young, Michael, English politician and sociologist, author of *The Rise of the Meritocracy* (1958), 13

Ziggurat, ancient Babylonian temple tower, reminiscent of the structure of the Egyptian pyramids, but not an individual tomb, 14

Zola, Emile (1840–1902), French art critic, novelist, leader of the naturalistic school, author of *Les Rougon-Macquart* (1871–93, 20 vols.) and other works, 131, 135

KURT W. MAREK is known to everyone interested in archaeology by
his pen name, C. W. Ceram. But now that "Ceram" is returning
to his main interest as cultural historian and social observer, he is
also returning to his own name. Born in Berlin in 1915, Kurt
Marek was for many years connected with newspaper work and
publishing, first as a drama critic and then as editor in chief
of Rowohlt Verlag, a Hamburg book-publishing house. His first
book, *Gods, Graves, and Scholars,* completed in 1949 after five years
of research and published in the United States in 1951, brought
world fame to Ceram as a writer on archaeology. Thereafter, he was
frequently invited to join expeditions in the field. His book *The
Secret of the Hittites* (1956) was one of the results of two trips to
Turkey as participant in excavations uncovering the Hittite past. In
1958 he published *The March of Archaeology.* Since then the
writer who almost singlehandedly popularized archaeology has
turned from the past to consider our cultural future, speculating on
our progress in art, in literature, in science and technology, and
on our outlook in the space age. Mr. Marek lives with his wife and
son in Woodstock, New York.

August 1961

A NOTE ON THE TYPE

This book was set on the Linotype in Bodoni Book, a printing type
so called after Giambattista Bodoni (1740–1813), a celebrated
printer and type designer of Rome and Parma. Bodoni Book as
produced by the Linotype company is not a copy of any one of
Bodoni's fonts, but is a composite, modern version of the Bodoni
manner. Bodoni's innovations in printing-type style were a greater
degree of contrast in the "thick and thin" elements of the
letters and a sharper and more angular finish of details.

Composed, printed, and bound by
Kingsport Press, Inc., Kingsport, Tennessee.
Paper manufactured by
S. D. Warren Company, Boston.
Typography and binding design by

HERBERT BAYER